SKYROCKETING INTO THE UNKNOWN

SKYROCKETING
INTO THE
UNKNOWN

BY
CHARLES
COOMBS

Illustrated
with Photographs

WILLIAM MORROW and COMPANY

New York   1954

To
my three children,
LEE, DAN, and LYNN
. . . eager participants of a
jet and rocket age.

ACKNOWLEDGMENTS

In doing a work such as this, an author is dependent upon the amount of co-operation he receives from the various possible sources of information. It is, therefore, with great sincerity that I wish to thank the Douglas Aircraft Company, Inc., the National Advisory Committee for Aeronautics (NACA), the United States Navy, Air Force, and Marines, and all the engine and airplane manufacturers (most of whose names appear on the picture-credit page) for their boundless assistance in making this book possible.

I am grateful to Robert G. Smith, whose color painting graces the cover jacket and whose fine drawings are featured in the final chapter.

A most deep appreciation to my good friend Chester G. (Chet) Miller, without whose enthusiasm and ever-ready willingness to pitch in and help polish up the rough spots this book might never have been completed.

CHARLES COOMBS
Los Angeles, 1954

Acknowledgments for Photographs

CONTENTS

ILLUSTRATIONS

11

ILLUSTRATIONS

12

ILLUSTRATIONS

13

ILLUSTRATIONS

SKYROCKETING INTO THE UNKNOWN

I

WHAT'S THE BIG HURRY?

THE sudden loud bray of the warning horn fills the small cockpit of the Skyrocket. Red lights flash urgently beside the instrument panel.

Fire! A flier's most dreaded enemy!

Close to one of the scarlet lights the round dial of the air-speed indicator shows that the sleek, needle-nosed aircraft is whizzing along at over 700 miles per hour. The arrow of the altimeter snuggles far down near the fifty-foot mark. The skimming aircraft almost grazes the scraggly tops of the grayish-green sagebrush which speckles the flat, sandy floor of the California desert.

If there is any place in the world where a pilot would like least to be at this moment, it is the cockpit of the low-flying supersonic Skyrocket . . . with fire breaking out aboard.

A host of grim thoughts flash through the airman's

17

With rockets roaring, the Skyrocket zips across the desert floor in a low-altitude high-speed run.

mind. Yet, despite the urgency of the moment, they are calmly organized thoughts. During his years of flying aircraft of all sizes, shapes, and kinds, the test pilot has faced many critical emergencies. In none of these tight spots has he ever allowed the paralyzing clutch of panic to deaden his reasoning.

Now, with a speed of muscle that nearly matches the speed of thought, he acts. There is no point in attempting to look back to see where the fire has broken out . . . or trying to figure out how much of the airplane is burning behind him. Even if the answers could do him any good, the two small window ports in the Skyrocket's cockpit enclosure are not arranged to allow a rearward view. He can only act and hope that he does the correct things at the right times.

However, the test pilot is not completely unprepared for the emergency—far from it. Like a fighter training for a championship bout, he has spent many hours "shadow-boxing" the Skyrocket's controls while the supersonic aircraft was sitting safely in the hangar. He has memorized the location of every switch. He is acquainted with every button and every dial clustered around him. He has done everything humanly possible in the way of preparing his defense against a knockout blow. But this could well be it.

With co-ordinated thought and motion, the test pilot of the Douglas Skyrocket moves in several directions at once. He hauls back on the control wheel. He will need a few thousand feet of air beneath him in case he has to abandon the million-dollar test airplane and bail out in his parachute. Even as the sharp-nosed craft spears upward, the airman pulls the fire-extinguisher handle. He also kills the rocket motor, shuts off the fuel supply, and hits the necessary switches to deaden the electrical currents.

But there are still other things which have to be done during those brief moments when terror plucks at the pilot's sleeve. While still in his steep climb, he banks the plane sharply on one wing. He flicks another switch and radios the field that he is on fire and coming in. He does

The Douglas D-558-2, Skyrocket, was the first research aircraft employing both jet and rocket power. Also first major aircraft to test the swept-back wing.

not bother looking down to see if the ambulance and crash wagon are going to be on time to meet him. As a matter of fact, their drivers have hardly touched the starters by the time the Skyrocket comes swooping down toward the packed sand of the age-old desert dry lake.

ʹ The ground beneath rushes past like a giant gray blanket. But the test pilot knows it will not feel like any blanket if he makes the least error in judging his landing. Still heavily loaded with the dead weight of much fuel, his speed seems far too great for a safe landing.

When he touches down—and without benefit of power—the Skyrocket is clocking 240 miles an hour. This is probably an all-time record speed for a dead-stick airplane landing.

But the flier is not thinking about records. Shortly after the wheels touch the packed sand, a sharp rifle-like report echoes into the cockpit as one of the high-pressure tires is sliced on a rock which somehow got onto the smooth runway. Crippled by the blown-out tire, the Skyrocket totters, off balance. To lose control of the aircraft at such a high speed would almost certainly prove fatal.

At that moment a person of less courage and self-discipline might well have resigned himself to his fate and braced himself for a crash. But the highly trained test pilot fights it through, as he has fought through many another tight spot and lived to tell about it. His hands are sweaty and slippery on the steering yoke, yet he manages to hold his grasp. His feet work with delicate skill on the rudder pedals. Gradually and patiently, he coaxes the Skyrocket to a limping stop.

No sooner has the desert dust begun to settle than the pilot jerks the canopy release and vaults out of the cockpit. He is inspecting the fire damage by the time an excited group of scientists, engineers, and mechanics arrive.

One look at the pilot's smile—a rather tense smile, but a smile just the same—and the anxious technicians know he is all right. They turn their attention to the airplane, especially to the faulty exhaust assembly which caused the almost fatal fire. They carefully examine the blown-out tire.

Later, as the mechanics start to tow the Skyrocket away, the pilot hops into a waiting jeep and heads toward the cluster of flight buildings. As they roll across the broad expanse of hot sand, the young navy man who is driving the jeep turns to the airman. "Pretty close call up there, wasn't it?" he asks.

"Closer than I like," the pilot answers simply. "But I guess that's all part of the business of being a test flier."

"Mind if I ask you a couple of questions?"

"Shoot."

"Well, you were whizzing along up there at almost the speed of sound when the trouble started. Right?"

"Pretty close," the pilot says, smiling.

"What do things look like when you're going that fast?"

"Look like? Why, at that low altitude and that speed the ground goes past so fast that it's as if someone were spinning a high-speed grinding wheel in front of your eyes. Just a gray blur. Anyway, you're not paying much attention to the scenery."

"No scenery, huh?" the enlisted man says, as the jeep dodges a clump of desert cactus. "Well, just where were you going, anyway?"

"Going?" The pilot looks at him, puzzled. "Why, no place in particular. Why?"

The young driver shakes his head. "If you weren't enjoying the scenery and not going any place in particular, then do you mind telling me what was the big hurry?"

The test pilot laughs softly. A curious question but a logical one, at that. In fact, he has often asked it of himself after he has flirted with death at supersonic speeds, or has reached skyward toward the stars in the rarefied atmosphere where a man's blood would boil and he would literally puff up to twice his size and die in a matter of seconds if he were not protected by the pressurized cockpit and fed oxygen from a tank.

What's the big hurry? That's a good question.

Perhaps to many it seems like an unnecessary and extremely dangerous pastime, this high-speed-flying business. After all, what sensible person is ever going to be in such a frantic hurry that he is willing to travel through space at a thousand or more miles an hour to get there . . . at the risk of being roasted alive by the enormous friction heat created by the air brushing against his rocket plane? Also what is the purpose of flying many miles above the earth's surface, where there is no air to breathe and where the killing temperature hovers down around 65 degrees below zero?

As for scenery . . . well, from the height of ten miles or more all one can see is a tiny patchwork of browns, greens, and grays, with the thin blue threads of waterways holding the pattern together. Certainly there is more to be seen and enjoyed from the safer and saner altitudes of three or four thousand feet.

But there are many reasons for man's big hurry and for

Sprouting miniature wings and packed with an array of electronic instruments, this research body will test wing characteristics at supersonic speeds.

Shackled to an airplane, the weighted body is carried aloft and dropped from a high altitude.

Checked in flight by automatic dive brakes and then by parachute, the body is recovered unharmed.

his constant search into the upward reaches of the skies.

Man, filled with curiosity, has always been a restless creature. Seldom has he been satisfied with his lot. No doubt this is fortunate, for most progress is the product of such unrest.

Ages ago man grew tired of living in caves. He progressed to huts and tents and houses, then to villages and cities. He created great empires. But he was still restless and inquisitive. He searched for new lands. After finding them, he planted his colonies and moved on until there remained very few unknown, uncharted, or unclaimed lands in the world.

Still prodded by restlessness and curiosity, he explored the waters of the world. An air-breathing creature by nature, man even found ways to keep alive for short periods of time beneath the surface of the waters. Soon he had solved a great many of the mysteries of the underwater world and is solving more each day.

With the frontiers of land and water fairly well explored, man's interest was attracted to the most common of all his surroundings, the air above him.

The movements of the clouds and the flight of birds were things he had taken for granted down through the ages. There had been a few men, known as crackpots in their day, who dreamed of flight. Nearly 500 years ago, Leonardo da Vinci made sketches and even models of crude flying machines. In the 18th century the Montgolfier brothers built a clumsy-looking balloon. When filled with

Lighter-than-air craft, such as the dirigible Macon, contributed to aircraft history.

hot air, the strange lighter-than-air craft soared over the housetops of Annonay, France. That was about as far as aviation went for a long time.

Early scientists had been content to name air as simply an invisible, odorless, and tasteless mixture of "nothing" . . . but a "nothing" that was necessary to life. Later, chemists broke it down into elements—nitrogen (72 per cent) and oxygen (21 per cent) with the remaining 7 per cent made up of small quantities of many other known and unknown gases.

With Orville Wright at the controls, man accomplished his first successful flight in a heavier-than-air craft on December 17, 1903.

No longer satisfied with merely using air as something to breathe, man began probing deeper into the unexplored frontiers of the sky. For centuries he experimented with balloons, kites, and even clumsy uncontrolled rockets. He made use of the winds to turn his mills and grind his grain. In a rather primitive way he felt he was approaching at least a partial answer to harnessing the powers of the atmosphere. Yet he had barely made a beginning.

Then, from a sandy knoll at Kitty Hawk, North Carolina, on December 17, 1903, two brothers, Orville and Wilbur Wright, made the first controlled power flight into the sky. The flight lasted a brief twelve seconds, and was measured in feet (120) instead of miles. Its speed was approximately 7 miles per hour. The distance of the entire flight was less than the wingspread of today's largest transports.

But with that first flight in their flimsy craft made of wood, wire, and canvas, the Wright brothers accomplished an age-old dream of man. Since that historic day a large portion of human attention and effort has been directed toward penetrating the mysteries of the sky, man's greatest and final frontier of exploration.

So, as in all fields of human endeavor, man's inquisitive nature and natural lust for adventure figure heavily in the progress of aviation. Yet there are other important factors which promote and hasten the exploration of high-speed and high-altitude flight.

Science feeds upon discovery. Sometimes the discoveries are earned the hard way. In the case of the Skyrocket's flight, just related, the tire's unexpected blowout came close to resulting in tragedy. Luckily and skillfully, that was avoided. From the incident it was determined that the Skyrocket needed tires with additional nylon ply capable of carrying nearly 200 pounds of air pressure. Then even the "hottest" of landings could be made safely . . . as far as the tires were concerned. Later, such tires were specially made and installed. Variations of such improved tires are used on all of today's high-speed aircraft.

The weakness of the faulty exhaust assembly was corrected, not only for the Skyrocket but for all planes of that type in the future. And it was found that a 240 mile-an-

The rocket-propelled Bell X-1 was the first airplane to pierce the sonic wall.

hour dead-stick landing was possible in an almost wingless airplane weighing some 16,000 pounds, fully loaded—valuable information, indeed.

All of this data, plus thousands of other items, has been and is being distributed throughout the military and civilian aircraft industry. This unification program is typical of the American way of sharing information with anyone who will use it properly and apply it wherever it will do the most good toward peaceful progress.

Test aircraft such as the Douglas Skyrocket, the Bell X-1, X-1A, X-5, the Northrop X-4, or the even more recent Douglas X-3 and Bell X-2, cost well upward of a million dollars. Much of this cost goes into engineering research and planning before a single sheet of metal is cut or a rivet driven. The important new aviation data received from even a few successful flights far more than pays the cost. For example, from the flights of the Douglas D-558-2 (Skyrocket) alone, nearly 9000 scientific reports have been distributed throughout the aircraft industry, to small and large producers alike.

This sharing of knowledge for the common good not only furnishes the small manufacturer with information he could never afford to obtain for himself, it also speeds up the over-all aviation progress of our country and all other friendly countries.

The whole progress of aviation depends largely upon just such experimental flights as the one made by the Skyrocket over the California desert. It is well to note that such flights are not made for the purpose of breaking old records or establishing new ones. Such is not the intent of research aviation. When you read in the newspaper of an X airplane (X denoting research aircraft) being piloted to an altitude well in excess of 80,000 feet, you are awed by the accomplishment. When you read of another research craft slicing through the upper reaches of the atmosphere at the amazing speed of 1650 miles per hour, or two and one half times the speed of sound, you start thinking in terms of new records.

Naturally, any improvement in speed or altitude over the figures of the past constitutes a record of sorts. It is

The Douglas D-558, Skystreak, often nudged the sonic barrier, but never quite got through it.

spoken of as a record and written as such in newspaper accounts. It has little official importance, however.

The important items are: How did the aircraft react to the ultrasonic speed? What were the effects of the altitude or speed upon the pilot? How did the metals and plastics of which the airplane is largely made react to the enormous strains of the flight or to the frightening friction heat of high speed, called the thermal barrier? How did the rocket motor function? How does fuel consumption differ up high, down low, fast, slow?

These are samples of the hundreds of items which in-

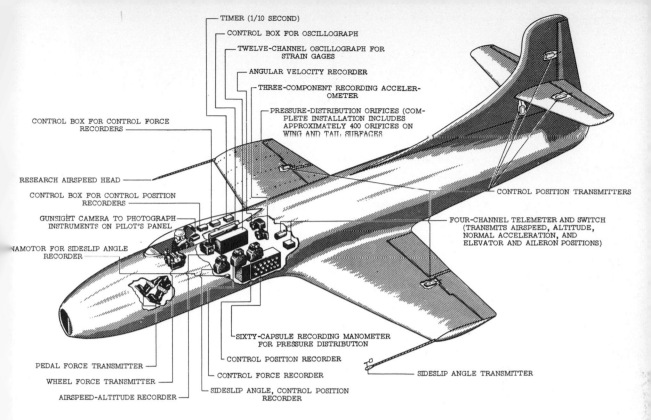

TIMER (1/10 SECOND)

CONTROL BOX FOR OSCILLOGRAPH

TWELVE-CHANNEL OSCILLOGRAPH FOR
STRAIN GAGES

ANGULAR VELOCITY RECORDER

THREE-COMPONENT RECORDING ACCELER-
OMETER

PRESSURE-DISTRIBUTION ORIFICES (COM-
PLETE INSTALLATION INCLUDES
APPROXIMATELY 400 ORIFICES ON
WING AND TAIL SURFACES

CONTROL BOX FOR CONTROL FORCE
RECORDERS

RESEARCH AIRSPEED HEAD

CONTROL BOX FOR CONTROL POSITION
RECORDERS

GUNSIGHT CAMERA TO PHOTOGRAPH
INSTRUMENTS ON PILOT'S PANEL

NAMOTOR FOR SIDESLIP ANGLE
RECORDER

CONTROL POSITION TRANSMITTERS

FOUR-CHANNEL TELEMETER AND SWITCH
(TRANSMITS AIRSPEED, ALTITUDE,
NORMAL ACCELERATION, AND
ELEVATOR AND AILERON POSITIONS)

SIXTY-CAPSULE RECORDING MANOMETER
FOR PRESSURE DISTRIBUTION

CONTROL POSITION RECORDER

CONTROL FORCE RECORDER

SIDESLIP ANGLE, CONTROL POSITION
RECORDER

PEDAL FORCE TRANSMITTER

WHEEL FORCE TRANSMITTER

AIRSPEED-ALTITUDE RECORDER

SIDESLIP ANGLE TRANSMITTER

A veritable "flying test tube," the Skystreak contains a maze of delicate
instruments which record each detail of every flight.

terest the makers of research aircraft and the pilots who
fly them. They prefer to leave the official records to the
men who fly production-model aircraft over measured
courses or at altitudes available to normal jet-powered
craft.

The research airmen are concerned only with probing
deeper and deeper into the slowly yielding frontiers of
flight. They want to find out what is up there, to investi-
gate the world beyond the sound barrier and climb the
first few rungs of the endless ladder into space. Their discoveries are of utmost importance to man's future in the
air . . . and beyond.

33

A slim, almost wingless sliver of aluminum alloys wrapped around its twin turbojet engines, the X-3 spears through the sky.

Perhaps one can say that man's instinct for self-preservation is another reason for this urgency felt by American industry to build such airplanes, and by American pilots to fly them faster and higher than those being built and flown in any other part of the world. In view of past world history, it would be an uneasy feeling to know that other countries had airplanes which could outspeed, outclimb, or outmaneuver our own. Superiority in the air is one of a nation's best forms of insurance for peace.

One needs to go only another hundred miles beyond the reach of present-day high-flying experimental aircraft to get into what is loosely called space. Space is the airless,

The primary purpose of the Douglas X-3 is to explore the field of supersonic flight at moderate altitudes.

lightless, temperatureless void through which man will some day blaze pathways to the stars.

But the space-hopping man of the future, like an earth child, must learn to walk before he can run. And space man is taking his very first toddling steps right now with his ultrasonic flights into ever increasing altitudes. Yet his great and amazing jaunts into the thinning atmosphere fifteen and more miles above the earth are hardly scratches upon the surface of unending space.

They are a beginning, though, a very important beginning. Scientists claim—and can support their claims with facts and figures—that even today an artificial satellite, or space station, could be constructed and set upon its own orbit around the earth. The cost and effort, however, would be staggering and, at this time, prohibitive.

This "second moon," once put into proper motion, would circle the earth endlessly. This is not guesswork. Impressive statistics compiled by the world's leading scientists add up to the following facts.

Before many years—but at enormous expense—rocket ships can be built which will carry men and materials out into space. Figures indicate that a space station could be assembled at an airless altitude of approximately 1000 miles. The earth's gravity still has effect at that height. If the space station were to stand still, it would be drawn quickly earthward, to disappear in a blazing meteorlike cinder once it reached the resistance of the earth's atmosphere.

The Northrop X-4 was one of the first research airplanes to test the tailless design of a flying wing.

The X-4 was a forerunner of flying-wing and delta-wing designs.

Bell Aircraft Corporation's X-5 is capable of varying the sweep-back of its wing while in flight.

A composite picture showing three possible positions of the X-5's variable sweep-wing . . . full out when taking off or landing, tapering rearward as speeds are increased.

With a Sabre jet tagging along, the world's fastest airplane, the Bell
X-1A, rockets through the substratosphere on a slow-speed test flight.

Looking not unlike something to be fired from a cannon, the Bell X-1A
carries sufficient rocket power of its own to enable it to pass a cannon
projectile in flight.

In order to overcome this pull of gravity, the artificial satellite would be put into motion. At the amazing speed of nearly 16,000 miles per hour, always maintaining its altitude of 1000 miles above the distant earth, the outward centrifugal force created by the high-speed circling around the earth would exactly balance the inward pull of gravity.

It can be likened to whirling a ball around your head on the end of a fine thread. The thread might be compared to the earth's gravity, preventing the ball from flying away into space. If you whirl the ball too slowly, it will cease its circling and fall to the ground. If you whirl it too vigorously, the outward force will break the thread and the ball will fly away. By properly balancing the whirling motion against the strength of the thread, there is nothing to limit the length of time the ball will whirl— except the fatigue of the experimenter's arm.

Since space has no substance or resistance which might tend to slow down an object, no further energy is needed, once the space station is put into correct motion, to keep it moving in the perfect vacuum of nothingness. Therefore, once such an artificial satellite is built, transported into space, and started on its own orbit, it will circle the earth endlessly like a new moon in our galaxy.

At the estimated speed and altitude, scientists figure that the space station will make a complete revolution of the earth every two hours. Since the earth revolves slowly on its own axis, every time the space station comes around it will pass over a new section of the earth's surface. By the time it has made 12 revolutions (24 hours), its inhabitants, from their 1000-mile-high vantage point, will have been able to view the entire surface of our planet. Close-up views may be obtained through the use of high-powered telescopes, radarscopes, television apparatus, and other means not yet devised.

It is further said that whichever nation first builds and mans such a space station will, from its lofty perch looking down into every nation's backyard, control the peace of the world. Any nation mobilizing troops or supplies for the purpose of an attack upon another nation would quickly be detected by the powerful telescopic eyes of the space station. By means of a radioed warning to nearby peaceful nations, the uprising could be quelled before it had a chance to get under way. As a last resort, should it become necessary, electronically guided bombs or destructive rays could be pinpointed onto any target from the orbiting space station.

As a peace-time function, occupants of the space station might look down upon the weather fronts of the world and make accurate weather predictions weeks or even months ahead. The space station might also serve as a jumping-off platform for space ships venturing toward the distant planets. Refueling and taking off from the space platform would eliminate the enormous fuel capacity now necessary in any attempt to escape the earth's atmosphere. If we had a craft capable of penetrating into space, it would now have to carry enough fuel to land on its distant destination and return to the earth.

There could be many a slip between penciled theories and the actual building and putting into motion of a space station. Yet top scientists in many fields are working on the various problems which they know will have to be answered. They are confident that each problem will have its answer and that shortly after the final answer is reached a space station will become a reality.

Certainly there are sufficient reasons and potential benefits to warrant the expense and personal risk that go into the present-day exploration of supersonic speeds and high-altitude flight.

Even if the reasons were lacking, man would still be busy turning yesterday's dreams into today's realities and tomorrow's probabilities. He would do this simply because the end has not been reached—not by any means—and man does not give up in the middle of an unfinished job.

2

WHAT'S UP THERE?

TOGETHER with willingness, courage, and skill, a large amount of curiosity is a great aid to anyone aspiring for a position on the small select team of supersonic and high-altitude fliers.

Near the top of the list of items about which he is curious, the test pilot wonders what he will encounter once he manages to get an airplane or rocket ship far out into the earth's atmosphere, or beyond it.

Many men and women are working on this problem. For every research flier in the air, there is a tremendously large and active crew of workers down on the ground. This crew is composed of planners, draftsmen, engineers, materials experts, metal craftsmen, mechanics . . . hundreds of specialists in every phase of the planning, designing, and building of an airworthy craft. To list these various specialists would take several pages of fine print.

High subsonic transports of the future will probably have a cruising altitude of 40,000 to 50,000 feet.

Yet if any one of the hundreds failed in his or her assignment, the entire flight project, risking lives and hundreds of thousands of dollars in equipment, could be wiped out in one tragic moment. There is extremely little room for error in the fields of supersonic and high-altitude flight.

Like a swimmer dipping an exploring toe into a pool before plunging in, science has cautiously been probing into the skies above our heads in order to know, at least partially, what is to be encountered by men and machines venturing ever farther upward. The findings are most interesting. Certainly knowledge of the skies is extremely important to anyone interested in the progress of aviation.

It must be understood that the earth's atmosphere is a definite part of the earth, just as the shell is part of an

Douglas F4D, Skyrays, slicing into the substratosphere.

egg. The ground is the solid part of the earth, the oceans, lakes, streams, and molten core are the liquid parts, and the atmosphere is the gaseous part. All three are equally essential parts of what we call Earth, or *Terra,* the third-closest planet to the sun in the solar system.

The atmosphere is made up of four loosely bounded layers. First is the troposphere, extending from sea level to around 40,000 feet. Next is the stratosphere, beginning where the troposphere ends and continuing to a height of about 60 miles. The third layer is the ionosphere, extending roughly from 60 miles to an altitude of 500 miles. The fourth and final layer, which is more space than atmosphere, is called the exosphere. Very loosely, this extends from an altitude of around 500 miles to the point where

45

the last few molecules of gaseous matter disappear and a vacuum of absolute nothingness exists.

For all practical purposes, space begins in the ionosphere at an altitude of approximately 120 miles. Here the atmosphere has thinned to such a degree that resistance to any moving body ceases and the only force slowing its speed is that of gravity. Technically, however, perfect space exists only after the very last atoms of the earth's atmosphere have been left behind. Theoretically, this point is reached some thousand or more miles out from the earth.

It hardly needs saying that we are extremely fortunate to have this protective layer of air around us. Without it all life would cease instantly, man, plants, and animals.

All forms of life depend upon moisture. Life would quickly perish without the atmosphere which carries this moisture and distributes untold billions of tons of water over the surface of the earth. It has been proved that even the very driest desert air contains a surprisingly large amount of moisture.

Moreover, without the protective blanket of dense air around the earth, the glaring unfiltered rays of the sun would burn everything to a crisp in a matter of minutes. Among these rays are the deadly ultraviolet rays thrown earthward by the sun. Yet although these rays are deadly in high concentrations, life depends upon the presence of a certain controlled amount of them. The filtering action of the atmosphere allows just the right number to sift

Rocket-powered test models are sent skyward to test the atmosphere's reaction on certain shapes. Results are recorded electronically from the ground and from within the vehicle itself.

through and reach the earth. X-rays, too, and various other cosmic rays, all of which would be deadly in large quantities, are partially prevented from reaching the earth by the all-important blanket of the atmosphere. Therefore, without this buffer of air to filter out much of the sun's power, the earth would be barren of all life. Furthermore, the atmosphere, during darkness, serves to hold much of the heat created during the day. Without the heat-absorbing blanket of atmosphere during the sunless night, the heat would dissipate itself into space and all living things would freeze in a sub-zero cold.

These theories, of course, are based on definite assumptions. If the earth had no atmosphere, heat would be created by direct contact of the sun's rays with an object and by that object's absorption of them. The amount of heat would be determined by the amount of absorption, which could figure in hundreds of degrees. Extreme cold would exist in the absence of those rays.

Such are the conditions believed to exist on the moon, which has no atmosphere—blistering heat where the sun hits, frigid cold where it does not, and no temperature in the surrounding space, for space itself can have no temperature.

Still another protective value of our atmosphere is the comforting fact that meteors plummeting earthward through space are quickly burned out by friction heat once they reach the comparative solidity of the air. Traveling at thousands of miles an hour, the meteors turn into flaming cinders on contact with the stratosphere. Occasionally a meteor is so large that part of it gets through to the earth before it is completely turned into a fiery vapor. Sample meteors on display at most museums attest to this fact.

Since it is estimated that millions of meteors burn themselves out each day before reaching the earth, it is not difficult to imagine the deadly bombardment there would be if they were not stopped by the earth's atmosphere.

Of equally important concern to man, plants, and animals is the fact that life cannot exist without oxygen to breathe. This oxygen is found almost entirely within the lower few miles of the earth's atmosphere.

Being made up of definite molecules of many elements, the atmosphere has weight, just like any other substance, no matter how thin. Since its molecules are spaced wider apart, the atmosphere has much less density and weight than water or earth. For example, a given piece of atmosphere weighs approximately one millionth as much as a piece of earth of the same size.

A column of air a foot square and reaching up to its outer limits in space would weigh in the neighborhood of one ton. Since air has weight, it compresses close to the earth, just as a stack of hay compresses itself toward the bottom of the haystack. Of this atmospheric weight, about three fourths is concentrated in the lower few miles of the troposphere. Slightly less than one fourth is contained in the stratosphere, with lessening traces in the ionosphere and the exosphere.

It is within the first seven miles of the troposphere that all life, as we know it, exists. The densest part of the troposphere, of course, is that nearest the earth, where it contains about 21 per cent of oxygen along with nitrogen and traces of many other gaseous elements. The higher one goes, the less compressed, or dense, the air becomes. Consequently, the molecules of the gases get farther and farther apart until, by the time one reaches an altitude of around 20,000 feet, the oxygen content has become so thin that it will no longer support life. From that point on up it becomes rapidly thinner until all trace of it disappears and true space begins.

Even before he reaches an altitude of 20,000 feet, a man must be supplied with oxygen from a tank or other artificial supply or he would quickly suffocate.

Beyond the troposphere, the stratosphere extends to an altitude of approximately 60 miles. Here there is no dust, not enough oxygen to be of any value, no smoke, fog, smog . . . or life. Yet man, by using his ingenuity, has done a considerable amount of exploring in the stratosphere. By using instrument-carrying rockets, man-and-instrument-carrying balloons, and even man-carrying airplanes, he has already learned a great deal about this stratum of the atmosphere.

Here is the area in which future high-speed flight no doubt will take place. In the stratosphere the air becomes so thin that it offers little resistance to any moving object. This allows craft to travel at high speeds which would burn any aircraft to a crisp if attempted in the lower regions of thicker air and consequently increased friction drag.

Since the stratosphere is far above the clouds, there is, of course, no danger of rainstorms, snowstorms, or other hazards encountered by low-flying aircraft. However, there are indications gleaned from weather balloons tracked by radar that extremely high winds sometimes buffet the upper regions of the stratosphere. Although this might prove a hazard to future planes flying at extreme altitudes, too little proven data is known of their existence and characteristics to make it worthwhile worrying about such winds at present. Besides, without the solid substance of air behind them, the winds might well prove to be no obstacle. A 400-mile-an-hour gale might not even have enough force behind it to rumple a man's hair.

In the lower part of the stratosphere, the area extending from 8 to 30 miles above the earth, the temperature hovers around 67 degrees below zero. Above this area it climbs rapidly up to a heat of 170 degrees at an approximate altitude of 40 miles. Here there exists a layer of ozone which absorbs a large amount of the ultraviolet radiation from the sun, creating its own belt of heat, but protecting the earth from a lethal bombardment of ultraviolet rays.

Beyond the ozone layer the temperature decreases. At

around a 50-mile altitude it is down to 28 degrees below zero. Once through this narrow belt of sub-zero cold, the temperature starts up again until, at an approximate altitude of 400 miles, it is estimated to be an amazingly hot 4000 degrees Fahrenheit.

The stratosphere ends at about a 60-mile altitude, and above that the ionosphere extends to a height of approximately 500 miles. Here the air has become so thin that only about one three thousandth of the total weight of the atmosphere is contained in the entire belt. The ionosphere is an area of great electrical activity. Here there is a constant and violent bombardment of cosmic rays—X-rays, gamma rays, ultraviolet rays, and others. A large portion of these rays is broken down into ions and free electrons. These energy-laden charges create great electrical activity. It is in the ionosphere that the electrical phenomena known as the northern lights and the southern lights take place.

It is this supercharged belt of the ionosphere which bounces radio waves back and forth to earth, making distant broadcasts possible. The shorter, sharper waves of radar, television, and high-frequency radio knife on through the ionosphere instead of being bounced back. That accounts for the limiting of television reception to areas located in direct line to a sending or relay station. If the ionosphere reflected back the short TV waves, as it does the longer radio waves, the downward-directed TV waves would reach all television sets, no matter where

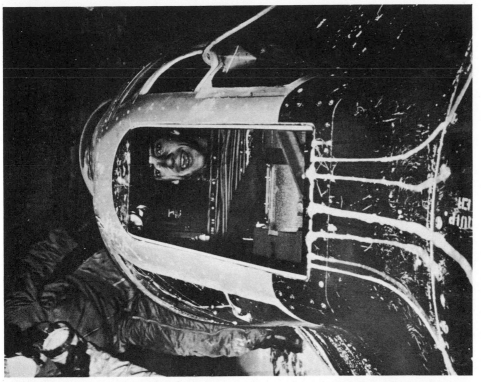

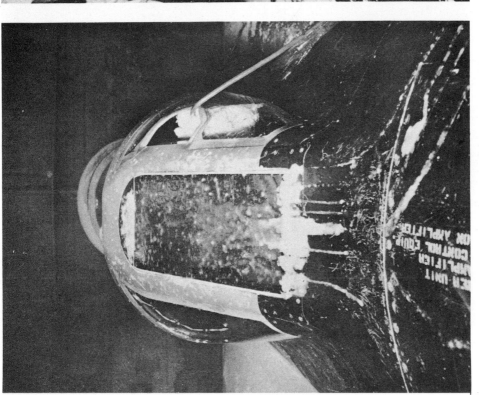

Testing and perfecting windshield deicing devices is an essential part of man's quest into the sub-zero temperatures of the upper atmosphere.

they were. Mountains or the curve of the earth's surface would not interfere with reception.

The fact that the ionosphere is unable to reflect back the sharp waves of high-frequency transmission has made it possible to contact the moon with radar. In the future, perhaps, it will allow uninterrupted communication between earth stations and space ships.

The temperature of 4000 degrees at an altitude of 400 miles is not as frightening as it sounds, since it exists only in the form of solar radiation. Solar heat does no damage unless it strikes and is absorbed by some object. Because the ionosphere contains practically no particles which might reflect or soak up the solar heat, the temperature is more a matter of theory than fact. But send an airplane up there, or anything else that would absorb the sun's blinding unfiltered rays, and it would literally be vaporized by the heat.

V-2 rockets have been propelled into the ionosphere. Carrying mazes of delicate instruments, they have brought back much valuable data. The WAC Corporal, which is launched from the nose of a V-2 in full flight, has pierced high into the ionosphere. The Martin Viking also has added much valuable information concerning the mysterious forces of cosmic rays, the filtering effects of the earth's atmosphere, and the plotting of pressures and temperatures in the various layers of air. These are partial answers to some of the problems with which future space travel is concerned.

Research rockets such as the Martin Viking are gradually solving many
of the mysteries of the outer skies.

Battery of Nike guided missiles. The missile itself is the upper half. Lower tube and vanes make up the booster, which drops off after the initial take-off.

Billowing smoke, the large-vaned rocket booster will soon drop away,
as the ground-to-air Nike guided missile continues upward.

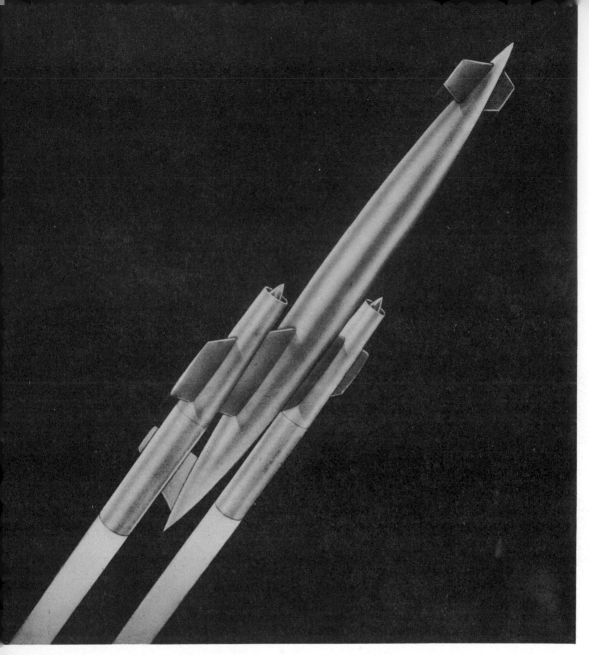

The design of today's guided missiles may be the design of tomorrow's space rockets.

Since the rockets have not melted and the animals sent up in them have suffered no ill effects (largely, perhaps, due to the fact that the rockets were painted a brilliant

Converted from wartime destruction to peacetime exploration, the German-built V-2's have furnished much knowledge of the atmosphere.

white, reflecting away the solar heat instead of absorbing it), men are encouraged to look forward to their own eventual safe journey far aloft.

The exosphere, the fourth and final layer of what we can still term a part of the earth's atmosphere, is, again, a very loosely bounded area, extending upward from the indefinite ceiling of the ionosphere. The exosphere is an area where weight and pressure and the few remaining atoms of gaseous matter slowly diminish and disappear, leaving a complete and perfect vacuum—space.

Although there are still a few scattered molecules of gases in the exosphere, they are too thinned out and inactive to form a friction barrier. Technically, space does not begin until the last atom of atmosphere has been left behind, but scientists, for practical purposes, consider everything above the 120-mile level of the ionosphere as space. And well they may. A thousand miles one way or another makes little difference when speaking in terms of space . . . or infinity.

Such is the atmosphere. It is the stuff (or lack of it) with which we must acquaint ourselves before venturing out to neighboring planets. Although we may look far into the future and envision days of stupendous speeds and quick journeys into millions of miles of space, we must be sensible enough to recognize present-day limitations. We must realize that it will take enormous amounts of time and effort and patience before dreams of space travel can become safe accomplishments.

The obstacles are all but overwhelming in view of present methods of power, types of fuel, limitations as to what the human body can withstand, and myriad other problems. Yet there is little doubt among practical-minded engineers, scientists, physicists, astronomers, and doctors that one by one these barriers in the pathway to faster and more distant travel will be overcome.

Indeed, we have knocked over quite a few of these barriers already. Each day brings some new element of progress. Vast sections of the fields of science, aviation, astronomy, and medicine are greatly concerned with lifting the celestial roof away from man's head so that he may find and explore and, perhaps, even inhabit new worlds.

But to repeat—the steps in this direction have been tiny compared to the giant strides which will be made in the future. Yet these first wobbly steps into the fields of supersonic and high-altitude flight are amazingly thrilling and important to the future of man's journey into outer space.

3

HOW DO WE GET THERE?

YOU do not need to glance very far back into the past to notice the enormous changes which have been made in aircraft design and methods of propulsion. Much of what seemed fantastic ten years ago has already become as antique as a Model-T Ford. Airplane speeds have increased so rapidly that a common hangar saying is: "If you can see it, it's obsolete."

During the past decade or so, drastic changes have taken place in aircraft design, particularly in military aircraft. Each change has been made with one general purpose in mind—to add speed, maneuverability, and striking power to the airplane. Even today most experimenting and testing of new ideas in aviation are undertaken with the needs of the military services foremost in mind. A majority of the tests are made with various government-sponsored "flying test tubes" such as the Douglas D-558 series, the

Orville Wright piloting a 1908 version of a "pusher" aircraft.

Bell X-1 series, the X-2, X-3, X-4, and the rest of the X craft.

This accounts for the fact that the first jet and rocket power plants were installed in military aircraft, rather than in planes owned by private airlines. It accounts for the fact that the first swept-back wings, the first delta wings, the tailless Northrop X-4, the Flying Wing, and the hundreds of other important flight innovations, both visible and unseen, were first built into military models.

This seems the only sensible way to do it. Experimenting in anything is an expensive process. American military aircraft are paid for by the American people's tax money.

A maze of struts and wire braces, the 1918 vintage Curtiss JN-4A, Jenny.

The Spad, a small single-seat fighter of World War I was seen stunting around the country well into the 1920's.

Since the American public benefits most by its country's leadership in the field of aeronautics, it seems proper that the people should share the burden of cost.

The progress of aviation has been steady and amazingly rapid, considering that man donned his first power-driven wings not much more than half a century ago.

As the old "Jenny" biplanes left over from World War I began to disappear, the fledgling flier began to feel more and more confident in his young wings. Eagerly the world launched full swing into the Air Age. Commercial and passenger aviation did not exist to any large degree. So then, as today, almost every important step in aviation was first tested out in aircraft of military design.

One by one the changes took place. Landing gear hanging down under an airplane created a great amount of drag on the plane during flight. This, naturally, cut down speed and consumed extra fuel. So the aircraft builders cut holes in the lower wing or fuselage, stuck hinged doors over them, and put extra hinges on the landing gear. By pressing a button or turning a crank, the wheels were folded up out of the way of the air stream. Thus the retractable landing gear was born. Disappearing wheels are now standard equipment on almost every type of aircraft.

Along with the disappearing landing gears there also vanished outside braces, wing struts, or anything else that stuck out into the wind to hold the ship back. Streamlining became the preoccupation of all aircraft designers.

In the 1920's the Dayton Wright Special Pursuit Airplane was the first aircraft to utilize a retractable landing gear.

The Boeing Model 40, one of the last of the commercial biplanes, established the all-weather practicality of carrying mail by air.

By the mid-1930's wires and struts had almost disappeared, wheels were retractable, and general streamlining was in use. Shown here is a Consolidated P-25, pursuit.

The more accurate the streamlining, the less wind resistance, so that the airplane could fly faster and farther on a given amount of power.

A needle pointed at both ends is a mighty neat job of streamlining. But since a needle can carry neither fuel nor passengers nor, indeed, fly under its own power, aircraft engineers had to compromise. Retaining as many of the needle's characteristics as possible, they have fattened out their craft, but never more than absolutely necessary. They have made it hollow, in order to lighten weight and in order to carry power, passengers, fuel and, if necessary, weapons.

As streamlining increased and aircraft engines became more powerful, radical wing changes took place. The big double wings of the old biplanes and even many of the large wings of the monoplanes furnished more lifting surface than was necessary to keep the aircraft in flight. Since too much wing merely increases drag, it robs the plane of speed and efficiency. So the wings were shortened more and more, in direct ratio to the increase in power which was being built into the newer engines. After all, if you have enough power, plus a method of controlling direction, you do not need any wings at all. But that is getting ahead of ourselves into the field of rocketry.

After the wings had been shortened down considerably, it was discovered that an airplane could travel still faster and create less air turbulence if the wing was swept back at an angle. Since a knife cuts better when held at an angle, it was correctly figured that a sharply swept-back wing would react the same way in slicing through the air.

One of the earliest models of military aircraft to try the swept-back wing was the North American F-86, Sabre jet fighter. Others followed. The swept-back wing soon became such an important improvement in high-speed aircraft that a rapidly growing number of military fighter and bomber planes now use it in one form or another. No doubt it will soon be incorporated into commercial transports and air liners.

The next progressive step was to sweep back the wing so much that there was no need or room for the usual tail

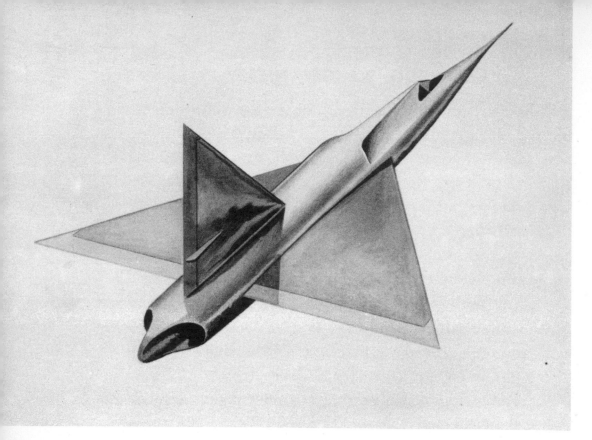

The shape of the present . . . and things to come.

surfaces. So the horizontal stabilizer was eliminated. Instead, the stabilizer controls were built into the trailing edge of a wedge-shaped wing.

This is the delta-wing design which already has been incorporated in Douglas Aircraft Company's recent bat-winged interceptor, the F4D, Skyray. Consolidated Vultee Aircraft Corporation went to similar extremes with its transonic fighter, the F-102 (formerly the XF-92A). The Chance Vought F7U, Cutlass, is a twin-jet, double-rud-dered, delta-winged speedster designed primarily for aircraft carrier use. An Air Force attack version of the Cutlass is designated as the A2U. England and other countries also have constructed and flown advanced delta-winged, high-speed aircraft.

The most important single factor making possible all this drastic modifying and streamlining of the aircraft itself is the enormous progress made in aircraft power.

The first forty years of aviation are a history of piston-type reciprocating engines and spinning propellers. A reciprocating engine is simply one in which a spark ignites a small quantity of vaporized fuel in a closed chamber (cylinder). The expanding hot gases created by the explosion push against a movable object (piston). This moving piston turns a crankshaft, which is geared to propellers or wheels.

But a piston-type engine has definite shortcomings. Certainly one of the big ones is the quite enormous vibration created by its plunging pistons and spinning cams. Besides, a piston engine requires an enormous bulk of more and larger parts to produce each additional unit of horsepower. After a certain stage is reached, the increased size of the engine necessary to create extra horsepower makes it too great to be of any worth in an airplane, where weight must be kept to an absolute minimum.

The function of the reciprocating type of airplane engine is, of course, to spin a propeller. The propeller, simply by screwing itself through the air, as a wood screw bites into a piece of pine, pulls forward whatever is attached to it. In the case of an airplane propeller, the object attached happens to be an airplane.

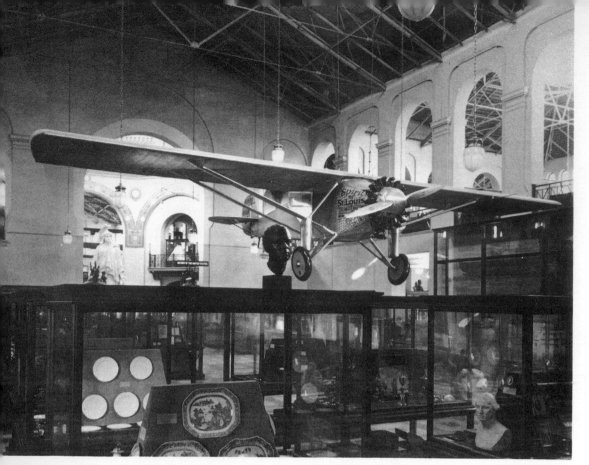

Charles A. Lindbergh's ocean-crossing "Spirit of St. Louis" is permanently preserved in the Smithsonian Institute.

However, the angled blades of the propeller, like the threads of a wood screw, must have something in which to bite. That something is air. But at increasingly high altitudes the air becomes so thin that the propeller blades cannot get a good bite. Consequently, the efficiency of the propeller drops rapidly at extreme altitudes. Fuel is wasted, and the valve-and-piston-type engine fairly beats itself apart creating wasted power. Even though self-adjusting propellers angle the blades so they will take a heavier chop on the rarefied air, there is still a great waste of power.

A similar problem is encountered at high speeds. The propeller is fairly efficient up to about 400 miles per hour. At higher speeds the efficiency drops off rapidly. This is due largely to the fact that the air is passing by so fast that the propeller does not have the opportunity to grab a firm hold. Like a screw in pulpy wood, the propeller starts "slipping threads" and, again, an enormous percentage of the power is wasted.

A piston engine also requires considerable amounts of oxygen in its diet. Oxygen is essential to combustion. No fire or explosion is possible without it. Therefore it is as necessary as gasoline in creating the rapid cylinder explosions which drive the pistons. For example, a pilot may climb to a high altitude where the air is thin and no longer offers much resistance to the forward motion of his airplane. But just as he is all set for his speed run his engine sputters and dies from lack of vital oxygen which, in the rarefied air, is absent in the quantity necessary to support combustion.

Engineers and mechanics were able to add a few miles per hour and a few feet of service altitude to the propeller-driven aircraft by harnessing the heretofore wasted exhaust gases of the piston engine.

First they piped the gas more directly rearward. In this manner the escaping exhaust formed something of a jet. This additional forward thrust helped a little, but not much. It did little to enable the aircraft to operate at high altitudes where the engine would cease functioning because of oxygen starvation.

Flying at higher altitudes became possible when the engine manufacturers developed a new idea for harnessing the exhaust gases. They put the gases to work by channeling them through a wheel made of many fanlike blades. As a breeze turns a windmill on a farm, so the exhaust spins the many-vaned wheel, which, in turn, is geared to a supercharger.

If a football team scattered itself all over the field, nothing would happen—at least, nothing that would result in a touchdown. But gather the separate players together, line them up in close formation, call the signal, and the team drives forward as a unit. A similar situation exists up high where the air is thin. The molecules of oxygen are scattered around and will not team up. The function of the supercharger is to compress the scattered molecules of oxygen into a useful concentration. Capable then of supporting combustion, the oxygen is mixed with the vaporized fuel. Ignited by a spark from a spark plug, the highly volatile mixture explodes into piston-driving action.

Therefore, with the supercharger to make thick, workable oxygen out of the thinly scattered molecules present in the upper atmosphere, the piston-driven propeller craft is able to operate at somewhat higher altitudes. But even the supercharger becomes a temporary answer. The propeller still does not get a firm enough bite on the thin air. And as the altitude increases, the supercharger is unable to gather together enough oxygen molecules to compress into a density sufficient to support combustion. With each hundred feet of increased altitude the air-gobbling piston engine becomes less useful. At the height of 55,000 feet a combustion engine's power output drops to zero. And that is a poor place to be running out of power.

The next step was to concentrate more upon the push of the exhaust than upon the pull of the propeller. Aeronautical scientists dug up an old law which had really never been buried very deep. As a matter of fact, all motion—forward, backward, upward, or downward—is governed by its principle.

Back in the latter part of the 17th century, this law was figured out by Sir Isaac Newton, the man who worked out the answer to the problem of why an apple falls downward when it leaves a tree. Apples had been falling off trees for quite some time before Newton's day, but he was the first one really to sit down and figure out the reason. The answer, of course, was gravity.

But Newton did not stop thinking there. He became extremely interested in all movement. In a short time he came up with the three famous laws of motion. At this moment, we are particularly interested in the third one. It states simply that every action going in one direction creates an equal reaction moving in the opposite direction.

The kick, or recoil, of a gun is a simple example of

how this law works. As the bullet rushes one way, it pushes the gun with exactly equal pressure in the opposite direction. Now if the bullet and the gun were of the same shape and weight (which, of course, is impossible), each would travel exactly the same distance in opposite directions. However, the gun is much heavier than the bullet, and the hunter's shoulder is behind it to absorb its backward thrust. Consequently, the backward reaction to the bullet's forward action is distributed and absorbed almost without notice. Besides, the open gun barrel allows the bullet to speed away unimpeded.

The fact remains, however, that the energy which propels the bullet forward (action) exerts the exact duplicate force backward (reaction).

Sir Isaac's third law of motion applies when you dive from a springboard. As you soar upward (action), the board bends down (reaction). The same force bends it downward that propels you upward.

Perhaps you have misjudged the dive and you take a belly flop. Your body smacking into the water (action) causes the water to splash out in waves (reaction). The splashing water retreats with the same force with which your sprawled-out body attacks it. This is all part of the third law of motion, even though it may not lessen the sting of the belly flop.

A clean heads-down dive, by its streamlining, would have offered less resistance to the opposing force—in this case, the water. Of course, even a clean dive would have created the exact opposite force (reaction) as in the case of the belly flop. However, the reaction force would have been more comfortably distributed, stirring the water deeper and less violently instead of just near the surface.

This more smooth and even distribution of the reaction force is the whole theory behind streamlining. On the other hand, the more rapid and violent the reaction—although always kept under control—the more efficiency there is in jet and rocket propulsion. For the entire field of jet and rocket propulsion is based strictly upon Sir Isaac Newton's third law of motion.

Blow up a toy rubber balloon and let it go, and it darts around the room. Hit a ball, and feel the bat tend to bounce back in your hands. The lighter the bat or the heavier the ball, the greater the effect of the reaction force. Hit a basketball with a child's toy bat, and the reaction force is so strong that it may tear the bat right out of your hand. Watch a hammer bounce back off a nailhead, and notice that at the same time the nail goes into the wood.

Do anything, make any motion, and you set two equal forces operating in opposite directions. Usually the reaction is so cleverly absorbed that you hardly realize it is there. When you throw a baseball you may wonder where the reaction is. It's there, all right. Part of the reaction of the forward throw is absorbed in the muscles of your body and arm. Although you are not aware of it, that slight recoil has helped to keep you from falling flat on your face in the direction of the throw. Although it is not visible, a good portion of the reaction of the throw is apparent in the air being driven out of the path of the speeding ball. Yet, in being driven away, the reaction force of the receding air exerts enough pressure against the action force of the ball to slow it down until its momentum is no longer sufficient to keep it on a straight course, and gravity pulls it to earth.

All continuous movement is a chainlike series of action and reaction. To repeat, wherever there is action in one direction, there is certain to be an equal reaction force in the opposite direction. All movement is based upon this principle.

Without understanding Sir Isaac Newton's third law of motion, no one can possibly understand the basic theories behind jet and rocket propulsion. In this age of jet and rocket power such ignorance would indeed be tragic, for these are the two modern modes of power which are fast rendering obsolete all former methods of propelling aircraft.

4

THE SIZZLING BLOWTORCHES

A JET engine is a rather simple affair in comparison with
the ignition, carburetor, and crankshaft of the piston-type
engine. The inflated toy balloon turned loose to dodge
around the room is one of the simplest examples of jet
power. The turbojet used in a majority of today's military
aircraft operates on the same principle, although obtain-
ing the thrust is not quite as simple a matter as blowing
up a balloon, releasing it, and witnessing the result of the
forward thrust caused by the air escaping rearward.

A turbojet consists of a large hollow tube, open at both
ends. Inside, it is divided into three main compartments.
A single spinning shaft, or rotor, in its center is a jet engine's only large moving part.

When a turbojet is operating, an enormous quantity
of air is sucked into the hollow nose, or intake. Once inside, the air encounters a series of fanlike blades set into

the forward section of the fast-spinning rotor. This is the compressor. The whirling fan blades keep pushing the air back deeper into the first compartment, squeezing it tighter and tighter toward the rear. Similar in action to the process of baling hay, this pushing and squeezing creates a chamber of tightly compressed air. The oxygen molecules of the air become heavily concentrated and are ready to support combustion when mixed with fuel and ignited.

The firing takes place in the second, or middle, compartment, which is divided into a number of small barrels called combustion chambers. As the highly compressed air is fed into the combustion chambers, fuel such as high-test gasoline or more newly developed and more highly explosive jet fuels are sprayed in to mix with it. Instantly a spark plug ignites the mixture of compressed oxygen and fuel, and it explodes.

The explosion of the mixture converts the fuel and oxygen into superheated gases. These blazing gases expand in almost direct proportion to their heat. Immediately they must escape somehow out of the combustion chambers, or the pressure of their expansion would blow the engine to pieces. The only avenue of escape is toward the rear of the open-ended combustion chambers.

In their rearward escape, the hot swollen gases are channeled through a second series of fanlike blades. These blades form the turbine. In passing through, the superheated gases spin the blades of the turbine. Since the

Installing or removing a jet engine is equivalent to putting on or taking off most of the airplane behind the cockpit.

The jet engine sucks in and compresses vast quantities of air through its gaping mouth.

The Pratt and Whitney J-48 radial-flow turbojet is rated at nearly
6500 pounds thrust.

compressor and the turbine are on the same rotor shaft,
the flaming rearward-spurting gases do double duty, ro-
tating both the turbine and the compressor.

The frequency of the explosions, of course, determines
the amount of superheated gases, consequently the speed
of the turbine-driven rotor turned by the gases, and, to
a great extent, the amount of power produced. The cycle
of explosions in the individual combustion chambers occurs so rapidly that it produces a loud and steady roar.

Now to clarify a popular but false belief. It is not the
hot escaping gases pushing against the cool air outside that
propel the aircraft forward.

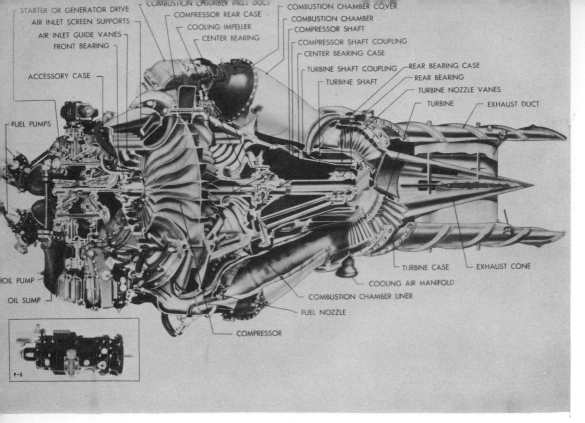

Labels on diagram:

STARTER OR GENERATOR DRIVE
AIR INLET SCREEN SUPPORTS
AIR INLET GUIDE VANES
FRONT BEARING
COMBUSTION CHAMBER INLET DUCT
COMPRESSOR REAR CASE
COOLING IMPELLER
CENTER BEARING
COMBUSTION CHAMBER COVER
COMBUSTION CHAMBER
COMPRESSOR SHAFT
COMPRESSOR SHAFT COUPLING
CENTER BEARING CASE
TURBINE SHAFT COUPLING
TURBINE SHAFT
REAR BEARING CASE
REAR BEARING
TURBINE NOZZLE VANES
TURBINE
EXHAUST DUCT
ACCESSORY CASE
FUEL PUMPS
OIL PUMP
OIL SUMP
COMPRESSOR
FUEL NOZZLE
COMBUSTION CHAMBER LINER
COOLING AIR MANIFOLD
TURBINE CASE
EXHAUST CONE

Cutaway view of the Pratt and Whitney radial-flow type turbojet.

Jet and rocket power is measured in terms of "pounds thrust" instead of horsepower. A pound of thrust equals one horsepower at a speed of 375 miles per hour. The ratio of horsepower rating increases at higher speeds, decreases at slower speeds.

The element of thrust, or push, begins in the combustion chambers, but it is built up inside a third chamber, or tail pipe. As the gases are heated they expand enormously. In their attempt to find a way out, they exert great pressure against all surfaces. Meeting solid resistance at these surfaces, the gases next seek to escape along the route of least resistance, which is rearward through the open exhaust hole.

External view of General Electric Company's J-47-GE-23 axial-flow turbojet.

Cutaway view of the Westinghouse axial-flow turbojet engine, capable of producing over 5000 pounds of thrust at modern flight speeds.

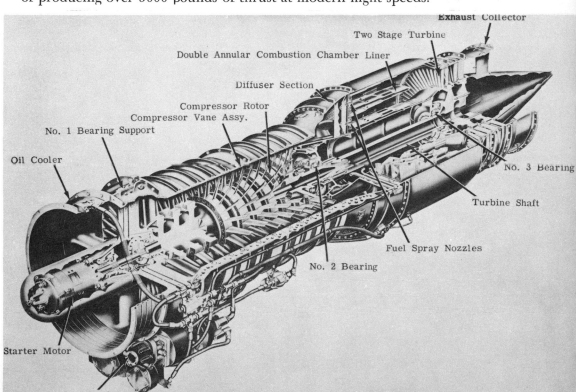

Exhaust Collector

Two Stage Turbine

Double Annular Combustion Chamber Liner

Diffuser Section

Compressor Rotor
Compressor Vane Assy.

No. 1 Bearing Support

Oil Cooler

No. 3 Bearing

Turbine Shaft

Fuel Spray Nozzles

No. 2 Bearing

Starter Motor

Accessories

As the swollen superheated gases press against the inner walls of the combustion chamber and tail pipe, another law of physics is brought into play. This law states that under no circumstances can two objects occupy the same space at the same time. The pressure of the expanding gases against the solid metal walls is, in effect, an attempt to displace the walls—to push them away and occupy the same space they occupy and more besides.

The surfaces inside the combustion chambers and tail pipe yield in an effort to escape the punishing pressure. Since they are built solidly enough not to burst, they take the next route of escape. The flow of hot gases has been directed rearward (action), so the logical direction for the metal surfaces to move in order to get away from the pressure is forward (reaction). It is this forward yielding movement which causes the entire jet engine, and consequently the airplane which is attached to it, to move ahead.

In order to get the most work out of the hot expanding gases, a cone is built into the tail pipe. The more area there is to push against, the more power will be salvaged from the crowding, shoving gases. So instead of just a small, flat bulkhead wall for the gas to push against, jet engine designers have built a tapering cone in the inside of the tail pipe, its tip pointing rearward. The hot gases surround it, pushing against its outer surfaces. So the tapering cone gives the superheated gases an additional surface area against which to push before they waste their final energy on the outside air.

THE SIZZLING BLOWTORCHES

When you squeeze an olive pit between your thumb and forefinger you are doing something similar to what the hot gases of the jet engine are doing to that cone. The cone can be compared to the pit and the expanding gases to the fingers pressing it. As the gas squeezes against the tapering walls of the cone, the cone squirts forward, taking with it, of course, the jet engine and the airplane.

So you have the pushing gas (action) and the airplane trying to get away from it (reaction)—a perfect example of Sir Isaac Newton's third law of motion at work.

The speed at which the gases flow rearward is called the jet velocity. Since the forward speed (reaction) is governed by the rearward speed of the flowing gases (action), jet velocity is the most important factor of rocket or jet propulsion. Of course, if the jet velocity is 5000 miles per hour, the aircraft's forward speed will not be 5000 miles per hour, although that would be the ideal situation. The airplane's weight, the resistance of the atmosphere, and other factors greatly reduce the forward speed. In space, where there is no resistance, scientists hope to achieve the perfect balance between the velocity of the rearward-escaping gases and the forward speed of the vehicle. In other words, they hope to convert each mile-per-hour of rearward velocity into a mile-per-hour of forward speed.

If you see a blowtorch-like flame squirting out of a jet engine, it is an indication of wasted power. For the escaping flame represents unused energy which should have been converted into forward thrust while still inside the

A cannon-like view of the power-increasing afterburners attached to the J-47-GE-17 turbojets at the General Electric Company's Lockland, Ohio, jet center.

engine. Jet engineers have already learned to harness much of this escaping gas by adding an extra chamber onto the rear end of a normal three-chamber jet engine. These fourth chambers are called afterburners. Additional fuel is sprayed into the afterburner with the escaping gases and ignited. Since the gases still contain enough unburned oxygen to support further combustion, additional heat—which means additional thrust—is created in the afterburner. The only drawback is that the afterburner enormously increases fuel consumption; therefore it is used only in short bursts when the need for extra power and

The Pratt and Whitney turboprop engine adds propeller power to its
jet thrust.

speed is critical. If the jet engine is built with an afterburner, thrust is, of course, created in both the third and
fourth chambers.

One popular variation of the turbojet power plant is
the turboprop engine. This is simply a jet engine with a
propeller attached to the front. Since the same rotor drives
the turbine, the compressor, and the propeller, the expanding hot gases perform a triple duty. The pulling power
of the propeller aids in takeoffs and during moderately
high-speed operations. But at extremely high speeds and
high altitudes, where the jet does its best work, the pro-

peller becomes more of a hindrance than a help. Therefore, the turboprop engine is fast disappearing in high-speed planes in favor of the straight jet.

Another type of jet engine is known as the ramjet or, as it is commonly called, the flying stovepipe. The ramjet has no moving parts such as a spinning turbine or compressor. It operates on a very simple principle. The air enters the tube through a narrow intake at the nose. The forward motion of the speeding airplane itself forces the air back into the cylinder, compressing it tightly. Then the fuel is injected, and a spark plug sets off the mixture. Again the explosions convert the fuel-and-air mixture into superheated gases, which expand enormously before escaping rearward and so move the plane ahead.

But a ramjet will not operate until the aircraft has reached a speed high enough so that the forward motion is sufficient to ram the air back tight into the combustion chamber. Depending upon the type of ramjet, this essential speed can vary from 200 to 400 miles per hour. Obviously, the airplane must carry some other source of power to provide the speed at which the ramjet can take over.

Due largely to the fact that very few aircraft manufacturers find it wise to add the extra weight and expense of carrying two types of engine in one airplane, ramjets are not in wide usage on airplanes. They are, however, used extensively in guided missiles. This is possible because a guided missile often gets its initial speed through the use

A simple stovepipe-like ramjet engine is prepared to be tested in a large supersonic wind tunnel.

The Pratt and Whitney J-57 turbojet is the first engine in aviation history to achieve an official power rating in the 10,000-pound thrust class.

of booster rockets. By the time the rockets burn out and fall away, the missile has reached a sufficient speed for the ramjet to take over.

With high speeds becoming the order of the day, a great amount of interest is being directed toward the possibilities of using ramjet power in future airplanes.

In short, the operation of any jet engine involves the basic process of drawing air in at the front, compressing it into many times its normal density, spraying in fuel, and setting a spark to the explosive mixture. The expanding hot gases pushing against the inner surfaces produce the thrust.

Most parts of a turbojet are within easy reach of workmen. These are Pratt and Whitney J-57's.

When the men are out and the cover is down over the test cell, this jet engine will be subjected to tests to determine its full range of power and reactions to high altitude.

It is quite obvious, therefore, that the entire working theory of a jet engine involves the use of large quantities of air containing the oxygen necessary to support combustion. A piston-powered aircraft, however, loses efficiency at altitudes where a jet craft operates very well. Even where the atmosphere is too thin to allow a reciprocating engine to operate at all, the jet functions nicely. The reason is that its enormous compressor can squeeze together enough oxygen to support combustion in altitudes where there is not enough oxygen for a piston-type engine. The thinning air of high altitudes exerts less friction resistance upon the airplane. With this decrease of drag, faster speeds become possible. Hence, the jet's favorite operating altitude is around 35,000 feet, far above that of the propeller-driven craft, which sticks closer to the 20,000-foot level.

But the jet's altitude is also limited. Progressing farther upward, the jet soon reaches an altitude where the oxygen molecules are so widely scattered that even the compressor cannot gather enough of them together to support the fire in the combustion chamber. Here the jet engine, too, loses its efficiency. This condition occurs at around 50,000 feet. Some newer jets such as the Pratt and Whitney J-57, used in the Super Sabre, the Skyray, and others, employ twin rotors which spin dual compressors, increasing both power and high-altitude efficiency. Basically, however, at 60,000 feet today's jet engine fails completely.

However, man finds an answer to most things. The answer he is finding to the problem of power at extremely high altitudes—altitudes, in fact, reaching into unending space—is the rocket.

5

ROCKETS AWAY!

THE theory of the rocket is identical to that of the jet engine. It is based on the process of burning a highly explosive mixture in a combustion chamber to provide expanding gases which force the body of the rocket forward out of their way. However, there is one main difference in a rocket. Unlike all the types of engines discussed in the previous chapters, the rocket does not need to gobble up vast quantities of outside air in order to squeeze together enough atmospheric oxygen to support combustion.

Even the rocket, however, cannot change the fact that there must be oxygen if there is to be a fire. Certainly if there is no fire, there is not going to be any of the expansion of gases necessary to propel the rocket forward.

The answer to this problem is simple. The rocket carries its own form of oxygen. This is known as an oxidant, or oxidizer. Quite often this is plain concentrated liquid oxygen, known among aeronautical men as "lox." There are numerous mixtures and variations of oxidizers in use and in experimental stages. The aim is always to find an oxidizer which will take up the least amount of space, yet create the hottest fire when it is mixed with the fuel and exploded in the combustion chamber.

Rocket fuels are sometimes simple, sometimes highly complicated mixtures. Some are composed of an alcohol-and-water solution. Concentrated hydrogen, acetylene, or even gasoline are sometimes used. Some carry names like *hydrazine* or *thiokol*. There are numerous other rocket fuels, whose compositions and characteristics remain secret. Their purpose, however, never varies—to create the hottest and quickest fire possible when mixed with the oxidizer and exploded. The purpose is also to maintain this fire by using the absolute minimum amount of fuel.

This is no simple trick. The present great shortcoming of rocket motors is that they consume vast quantities of expensive fuel mixtures in an amazingly short time. As new fuels are discovered which will furnish increased power per gallon, rockets will find their way into military, commercial, and interplanetary flying craft. This enormous fuel appetite is the rocket engineer's biggest problem. It is assumed that some day atomic power will be harnessed for this purpose.

Thus far the use of rocket motors has been confined in large part to unguided and guided missiles. These range from the bazooka projectile (a "dry-fuel" rocket contain-

Powered by a rocket motor capable of producing 20,000 pounds of thrust
at ultra-high speed, a Navy Viking leaps skyward from the deck of the
U.S.S. Norton Sound.

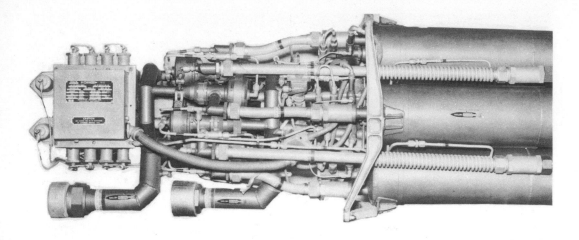

Although most rocket engines are still in the top-secret category, this is the RMI four-tube liquid-propelled rocket motor used in the Bell X-1, X-1A, Republic's F-91, the Douglas Skyrocket and others. Weighing a mere 210 pounds, the RMI develops upwards of 6000 pounds of thrust.

Cocked at a 30-degree angle, an RMI-series rocket engine simulates a full power-on dive.

McDonnell Aircraft Corporation's KDH-1, Katydid, is a radio-controlled, jet-powered target drone which cruises the skies giving gunnery crews something to shoot at.

ing its fuel and oxidizer in one compound such as cordite—a mixture of guncotton and nitroglycerine) to the German-built guided V-2, which spanned the English Channel with rather poor accuracy during World War II.

In the years since the war, rocket research has become a leading item in every country's defense program. Guided missiles are not piloted by human passengers, but are so designed that they hunt their targets electronically—by means of radio, radar, or television. Some are rocket-powered; some are jet-propelled. Some employ booster rockets to obtain the initial momentum, after which the rockets automatically drop off and a jet engine takes over.

101

Up to 24 rocket missiles can be fired from a retractable launching pod projected beneath the F-86D and subsequent model Sabre jets.

These guided missiles are divided into four main groups. The first is the air-to-air type. This is launched from an airplane toward a flying target, such as another airplane or some sort of flying missile. So accurate are the homing mechanisms in some missiles of this type that the rocket follows and catches its target, no matter how hard the target tries to dodge. The rocket's explosive warhead does the damage on contact or, if equipped with a proximity fuse, explodes short of contact but close enough to do its lethal work.

The Chance Vought Regulus is a remote-controlled jet-powered ground-to-ground type guided missile.

Then there are the ground-to-ground missiles, such as the German V-2, the more modern B-61 Martin Matador, Chance Vought Aircraft Company's Regulus, and other variations. These are launched from a ground site or from a ship's deck. With their flight controlled mechanically from afar, they travel over land or water, to drop finally upon their target. They are, in a strict sense, pilotless bombers.

Ground-to-air guided missiles are glorified antiaircraft weapons with the added feature of being able to search

Booster rockets help the Regulus get into the air, then drop away as the jet engine takes over to power the pilotless guided missile toward its destination.

Getting its initial boost from rocket power, the Martin B-61, Matador, will finish its pilotless flight with jet power.

out and catch their flying targets. These targets can be enemy aircraft or other air missiles. They can be flying on a clear day or be hidden deep in clouds. But they cannot hide from the electronic brain of the ground-to-air guided missile, which catches up to them and destroys them regardless of the weather or their evasive tactics. The Fairchild Lark and the Douglas-built Nike are two of the better-known ground-to-air guided missiles. Boeing Airplane Company's jet-powered F-99, Bomarc, is also a worthy member of this group.

The Boeing F-99, Bomarc, electronically seeks out and destroys enemy aircraft in the sky. A jet-powered ground-to-air type guided missile.

The fourth type of guided missile is the air-to-ground variety. This is actually a guided bomb. It may even have wings and a tail, plus its own rocket or jet power which permits it to be guided directly to any ground target once it has been dropped from the shackles of a high-flying bomber. Like that of a dropped bomb, the air-to-ground missile's course is always downward. But its electronically guided, powered glide is far different from and enormously more accurate than the free fall of an ordinary bomb.

Not all guided missiles are used for purposes of defense or war. Variations of the V-2 were the first man-made

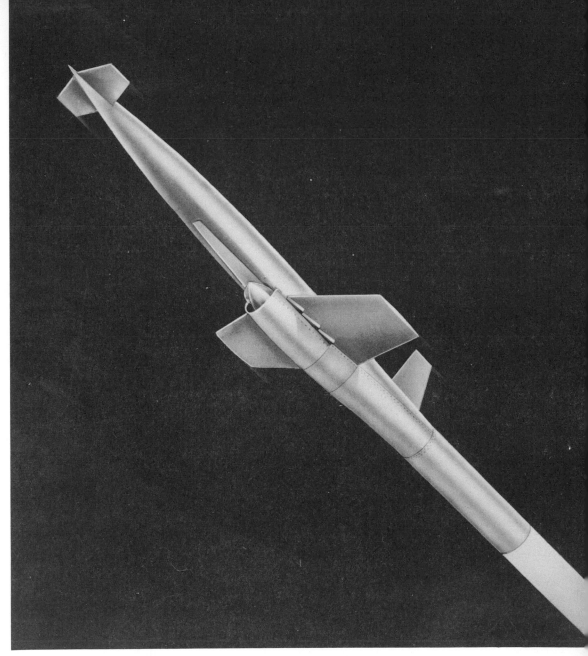

This tail-first design is one of the many variations being tested in the field of ground-to-air research guided missiles.

After the Lark has gained initial momentum, the square guiding vanes
and the booster rockets drop off and its own rocket motor powers the
remainder of its electronically directed flight.

Secrecy veils most rocket projects. This is an early-morning silhouette
of the Fairchild Lark, a ground-to-air guided missile.

missiles to reach beyond the stratosphere and well into
the ionosphere. Modified V-2's have reached altitudes of
over 120 miles—the practical beginning of space—before
their fuel and upward-coasting momentum were exhausted
and they parachuted back to earth, loaded with valuable
instrument readings.

Some years ago a smaller rocket known as the WAC
Corporal was fitted into the nose of a V-2. After the V-2
blasted off, the WAC Corporal rode along quietly until
the larger rocket began to lose its power. Automatically,

the WAC shot away from the V-2's nose, adding its own velocity to that of the V-2. The WAC Corporal exhausted its limited supply of fuel in a matter of seconds, but by the time it reached burnout (when the last drops of propellant coughed through the rocket tubes), it was high enough and traveling fast enough in the near vacuum of space so that it coasted many miles before the earth's gravity slowly pulled its nose downward.

In this manner the WAC Corporal reached the astonishing height of 250 miles. Its many delicate instruments brought back much valuable information concerning the amounts and kinds of radiation encountered in lower space. Its instrument-recorded statistics concerning varying temperatures, pressure, composition of the atmosphere, and other data were of great importance.

The Martin Viking, a single-stage true rocket, has pierced the atmospheric regions of eternally black skies to a height exceeding 150 miles. Its repeated flights have furnished us with invaluable data concerning cosmic rays, the effect of altitude on the earth's magnetic field, spectograph information on the sun's power out beyond the filtering effects of the earth's heavy atmosphere, and other partial answers to our many questions concerning space.

Almost every week, new rockets are making deeper penetrations into outer space. But most of the information concerning their performances and discoveries remains highly secret, to be released when it will do the most good for the most people.

McDonnell Aircraft's experimental RTV-2, Gargoyle, is a radio-controlled bomb of the air-to-ground category of guided missiles.

The field of rocketry is still in its infancy. But men who know agree that rocket propulsion is the answer not only to the problem of future world-spanning journeys through our own upper atmosphere, but also to the problem of man's eventual conquest of outer space.

To a less curious and determined creature than man, the enormous obstacles might discourage exploration into the unknown regions of supersonic speeds and the cold, dark voids of limitless space. But what not long ago was considered one of the chief obstacles has already been fairly well overcome. This is the much-referred-to sonic barrier.

The early belief held by many aeronautical scientists was that if an airplane caught up to the violent shock waves of its own sound, it would disintegrate like an egg thrown against a stone wall. The factor, they believed, which would cause this sudden and explosive smashing up of plane and pilot was the mixture of compressibility and shock waves. No matter how streamlined an aircraft may be, it still pushes some air ahead of it. This may be compared to the small waves that form ahead of even the sharpest prow a boat can have.

It was figured that when this compressed "bow wave" of air pushed ahead of the plane caught up to the shock waves of its own sound, a disastrous turbulence in an almost solid form would result. This sonic barrier became a discouraging prospect to high-speed fliers.

Yet it could not be denied that rockets such as the V-2 had pierced the barrier of sound many times. High-caliber rifle bullets had been doing it for years. But there was built into these missiles a streamlining and solidness which could not be put into the lighter airfoils of winged, man-carrying vehicles.

Still, interested aerodynamicists and engineers always came back to the belief that if rockets and bullets could do it, a piloted aircraft could also be constructed which would carry man safely through the sonic barrier.

So with practically no hesitation aircraft men accepted the challenge. Like crusaders starting out to storm a castle fortress, they set out to assault the sonic wall. That they were successful is a matter of history, a fine testimonial to the value of taking in stride the approach to and solution of each problem.

Today much is known about the sound barrier . . . and much is still unknown. As an object travels forward it sends out rings of sound-carrying shock waves in all directions. At sea level the speed of these sound waves is 760 miles per hour. At a 40,000-foot altitude, where the air is thinner and the temperature below zero, the sound waves do not propagate as readily. At that altitude sound travels at a slower speed—660 miles per hour.

Air is like a fluid. As an airplane travels through it, it moves smoothly over the surfaces of the craft, although some of it is pushed forward, forming the previously mentioned bow waves. The faster the airplane's speed, the more concentrated and "solid" become these bow waves of air. This is known as compressibility. When the air pushed ahead of the plane is compressed to a maximum density, it forms a veritable wall.

The point at which this wall occurs is when the speed of the plane matches the speed of the sound waves being sent out in all directions by the plane. When the plane travels as fast as the invisible waves of sound, the mixture of compressibility and sound waves creates violent shock waves. These shock waves are plainly visible in laboratory tests conducted in supersonic wind tunnels. Pilots of high ultrasonic airplanes have also reported seeing the shock waves forming off their wings.

This is the sonic barrier which, a few short years ago, was believed to be impregnable, but which crumbled under man's determined efforts.

Perhaps *crumbled* is a poor word to choose. For the hazards of the sonic barrier are still very real and dangerous. None of the many fliers who have successfully flown through the wall forget it, and today this accomplishment is routine, even among "hot" pilots whose flights are not devoted to research. For example, pilots of the F-100, Super Sabre, frequently crack through the sonic barrier in the course of normal operational flight.

It is not, however, quite as simple as falling off a log. The rather extreme turbulence reacts strangely upon the airplane. The wings flutter and the craft tends repeatedly to surge ahead and slow down as the shock waves form on the wings and fuselage and "tear away in uneven chunks."

Rudder, elevators, and ailerons often fail to function properly. Sometimes the controls actually reverse their purpose. If the pilot pulls back on the stick in order to climb, the airplane may tuck under in a dive. Sometimes the controls cease to have any effect. The pilot must constantly improvise at the stick and rudder pedals in order

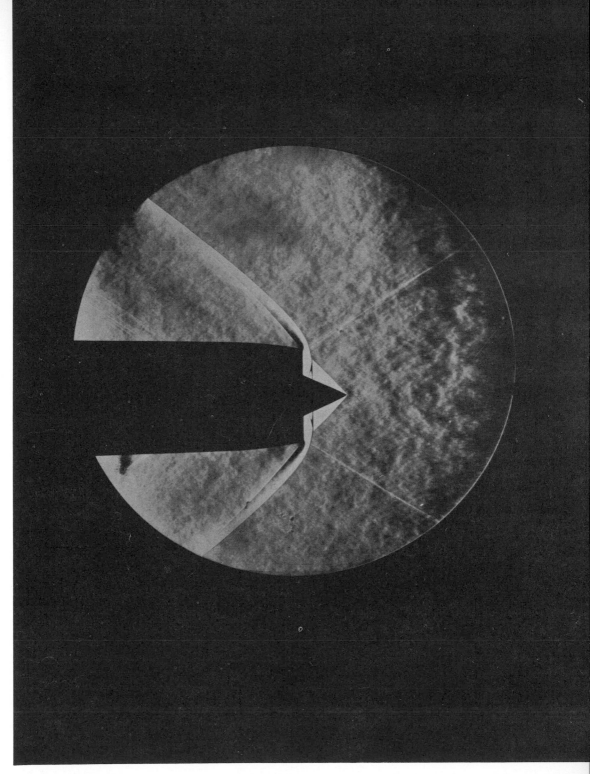

A special optical device permits a visual study of supersonic shock waves forming around the air inlet of a ramjet engine undergoing wind-tunnel tests.

to maintain something that resembles normal flight.

Daily, as knowledge is gained and revisions are made in aircraft design and pilot training, the hazards of the sonic barrier are being minimized. Knowing pretty much what to expect when he reaches the wall, a flier is equipped mentally and physically to cope with it.

In fact, today the terms *barrier* and *wall* are seldom used. Although this does not eliminate its existence, it has been leaped so many times and so much has been learned about its hazards and how to handle them that modern pilots hold it neither in awe nor fear.

6

AMERICA'S FINEST

PRESENTED on the following pages, in pictures and captions, is a comprehensive representation of the jet- and rocket-powered aircraft built in the United States.

These are America's finest!

The single-jet Grumman F9F Panther, first jet aircraft used by the U.S. Navy, has folding wings and strength to withstand the rigors of deck launchings and landings.

An underside view silhouettes the strength and clean build of the Navy's
Grumman Cougar.

Grumman's **F9F-6 Cougar** is the high-powered, swept-wing successor
to the Panther. This heavily armed Navy and Marine jet fighter is
equally effective as a carrier or land-based attack plane.

North American's FJ-2 Fury, a swept-wing carrier-based fighter, has over 5800 pounds of thrust. Rated in the over-650 miles per hour class, the Fury has a range of over 1000 miles and an operating ceiling in excess of 45,000 feet.

With its catapult cable kicked free, a Fury steps off into the sky from the flight deck of a carrier.

The Chance Vought A2U is powered with twin Westinghouse turbojets, each having power-boosting afterburners. Of the tailless, slightly delta-winged variety, the A2U is a superspeed (over 650 mph) fighter.

For aircraft carrier compactness, the Navy F7U Cutlass folds itself into
a small thin package of potential winged dynamite.

Heavily armed with machine guns, rockets, and bombs, Republic's
F-84E Thunderjet is a single-engined, high-speed, and highly maneu-
verable fighter-bomber. Jettisonable wing tanks increase its range to
1700 miles.

The F-84G, a slightly later variation of the Thunderjet, is the first fighter aircraft equipped for mid-air refueling. Here it fills its four 230-gallon external fuel tanks from a Boeing KB-29 tanker employing a flying boom to transfer the jet fuel.

The swept-winged F-84F Thunderstreak is the latest in Republic Aircraft Company's fighter line. It is equipped for in-flight refueling.

Packing 24 high-velocity rockets plus additional secret armament, the Thunderstreak is a pint-sized fortress of flying speed and strength.

The F2H-2 Banshee is a shipboard fighter built for the U.S. Navy. Powered by twin jets, this airplane uses jettisonable wing tanks for extra range.

The Banshee comes in several varieties—with radar nose as a night fighter or with elongated camera-carrying nose as a photo reconnaissance plane as here shown.

Powered by two Westinghouse axial-flow jet engines, Lockheed's F-90 penetration fighter is a long-range, high-speed, and versatile striking arm of the Air Force.

The McDonnell F-88A Voodoo is another twin-jet fighter capable of carrying its striking power far within enemy territory.

Still top-secret in respect to the details of its make-up, the McDonnell F3H-1N Demon is a super-speed, needle-nosed, swept-winged Navy jet fighter.

In a test flight, the Demon, followed by a chase plane, streaks through the sky too fast to be caught by the camera's eye.

The Navy Douglas F4D-1 Skyray is the first supersonic fighter-interceptor. The bat wings fold for compactness in storage. Powered by a single turbojet.

The Skyray presents a strange appearance from overhead.

The Douglas F3D Skyknight is a twin-jet, all-weather fighter-bomber. Carries pilot and radar operator, who doubles as navigator and bombardier.

Folding wings enable more Skyknights to be packed aboard an aircraft carrier.

Consolidated Vultee's F-102 is a delta-winged jet dart capable of supersonic speeds.

With a fuselage composed primarily of a jet engine capable of producing over 5200 pounds of thrust, the F-102 comes in for a normal landing.

The Consolidated Vultee XF2Y-1 Sea Dart is the first combat-type aircraft equipped with hydro-skis. Powered by two Westinghouse turbojets.

A great wake is left by the Sea Dart as it stands up on its hydro-skis preparatory to taking off.

North American Aviation's F-86D all-weather interceptor is a late variation of the famous Sabre jet line. Powered by a single turbojet engine with afterburner, the radar-nosed Sabre carries two dozen Mighty Mouse rockets plus other armament.

An enemy's-eye view back into the lethal gun-filled nose of the F-86F,
one of the latest of the USAF'S versatile Sabre jet line.

North American Aviation's F-100 Super Sabre has a 45-degree sweep of wing and tail. It has an operating ceiling above 50,000 feet and a combat radius in excess of 500 miles.

Feeling carefully for the ground, a supersonic F-100 Super Sabre comes in for a high-speed landing. Carries a parachute brake to aid in short-field landings when necessary.

The F-89D Scorpion, equipped with wing-tip rocket pods carrying an undisclosed number of rockets, is the most heavily armed interceptor-fighter of the U.S. Air Force.

Republic's XF-91 high-altitude, all-weather interceptor utilizes a turbo-jet with afterburner as primary source of power, and also carries a rocket engine to furnish added thrust and speed at critical moments. The sharp-edged, swept-back wing is able to vary its angle of tilt in flight.

Equipped with jettisonable external fuel tanks having a 500-plus gallon capacity each, the XF-91 adds great range to its protecting prowess against invaders.

Lockheed's F-94C single-jet Starfire is guided by its human pilot during the first stage of attack. Then electronic "brains" take over, locking onto the target, aiming and opening fire with the battery of rockets.

A fast flyer and fast lander, the Starfire carries a parachute brake which pops out of the tail to aid in stopping on short fields.

The Douglas A2D Skyshark is a powerful Navy attack bomber. Its turboprop engine adds the pull of two counter-rotating propellers to the push of its jet exhaust.

Martin P4M Mercators are long-range patrol airplanes, powered by the strange combination of two piston engines and two jets housed beneath them to add speed.

The Martin B-51 ground-support medium bomber is powered by three turbojets (two in pods hanging below the fuselage; one in tail). Crew consists of only two men—the pilot and a combination navigator, radio operator, bombardier.

A stick of 500-pounders drops from the bomb bay of North American Aviation's B-45 Tornado, a four-jet (two in each nacelle) high-speed Air Force bomber.

The Douglas A3D is the most powerful airplane ever designed for aircraft carrier use. It performs in the 600-700 mph class, and at altitudes exceeding 40,000 feet. The three-man crew includes pilot, pilot-bombardier, and gunner-navigator. Both wing and tail fold for compact carrier storage.

The U.S. Air Force's RB-66 jet reconnaissance bomber is close kin to the A3D. Armament and exact performance figures remain secret.

Boeing's B-47 Stratojet is powered by six turbojet engines generating a total thrust in excess of 35,000 pounds. The Stratojet has a range of 3000 miles at over 600 mph.

Eighteen built-in JATO rocket units, rated at a quick 1000 pounds of thrust each, give the Stratojet an emergency push to aid in short-field take-offs.

The Boeing B-52 Stratofortress, biggest and fastest jet bomber in full production, is powered by eight Pratt and Whitney J-57 jets mounted in pairs beneath the 185-foot swept-back wing. Built for high speed (over 600 mph), high altitude (perhaps above 60,000 feet), and long-range attack.

Despite the eight-wheeled tandem landing-gear brakes, the Stratofortress also carries a tail parachute to aid in bringing its mammoth weight to a quick stop.

Consolidated Vultee's YB-60 carries power similar to Boeing's Stratofortress, has a wingspan of 206 feet, a length of 171 feet, and a rudder
height of over 50 feet.

The real big boy of all the jet airplanes is Consolidated Vultee's YB-60.

7

NO *SUPERMEN* NEEDED

MEN have always wanted to share personally in an achievement, to be right on the spot when it happens. This not only gives a man the real thrill of adventure, it also allows him to pick up and bring back certain valuable information that no amount of delicate instruments could furnish.

Therefore, although remote-controlled rockets may reach the moon within the next twenty years or so (and this is a prediction made by scientists who should know), the moon job will not really be considered accomplished until a man steps out of a rocket ship and plants his own space boots firmly upon the strange soil of Luna, our nearest neighbor in the sky.

Today we have enormous exploratory rockets which pierce well up into space. Since they are unmanned, the information they bring back to earth is the impersonal data of graphs, instrument readings, and quantities of other "canned" details. This furnishes the man on the ground with a fair idea of what he would have encountered if he had climbed in and gone along on the space jaunt.

But the human body is a unique and highly complicated piece of machinery. There is only one valid way to determine how this body will react to certain unusual conditions and stimuli. That way is to subject it directly to those same unusual conditions and stimuli, or to reasonably accurate substitutes for the real thing.

In aviation this, of course, becomes the job of the test pilots. These men deliberately risk their lives in order to bring back all-important data concerning the human reaction to the rigors of high-speed and high-altitude flight.

But the lot of the test pilot is nothing like being thrown to the lions. Broken down into the simplest chemical elements, the human body is worth something under two dollars if weighed out element by element on a drugstore scale. An experimental research airplane is priced, in time and material, at something over one million dollars. Yet not one cent of these million dollars has been spent without keeping foremost in mind the safety and preservation of that scant two dollars' worth of mixed elements called man.

There are two basic divisions in the process of keeping a test pilot or any pilot, for that matter, safe. The first division is largely his own responsibility; the second is the job of aviation science.

NO SUPERMEN NEEDED

The pilot's physical condition is of primary importance. This is especially true if he is bent upon going places and doing things for which man was never intended by nature. On the other hand, any man venturing into the stratosphere, even if in the most perfect condition, would perish almost instantly upon exposure to the pressureless vacuum unless he was protected by every means known to science.

At high speeds, whether subsonic, transonic, or supersonic, an airplane often reacts strangely. The most unpredictable segment of the speed spectrum is the transonic zone. This is the area both approaching and just beyond the speed of sound. It is the area where the greatest turbulence is created by the mixture of compressibility and shock waves. Roughly, the transonic zone is considered to start at around 600 miles per hour and to disappear at approximately 800 miles per hour, where the true area of the supersonic zone begins.

A pilot must be in top mental and physical condition in order to be right on the job instantly with whatever human resources are needed to solve any emergency problem. Without this precise co-ordination of mind, body, and machine, a test pilot becomes a poor insurance risk.

Therefore, a test pilot—at least, a successful test pilot—trains as carefully as an Olympic athlete. He gets his full quota of sleep and keeps physically in tune through exercise. He eats wisely at all times and particularly before going "upstairs," where his body is going to have enough problems without adding chili beans and pie à la mode. He tries to keep his mind free from worries. A troubled mind may come up with the wrong decision at a crucial moment.

If the test pilot is not feeling in tiptop shape for any reason, no matter how seemingly trivial, he wisely keeps his feet on the ground.

He practices moderation in everything he does.

Locate a successful test pilot or any "hot" pilot and you will find a man who abides by these rules.

Yet mental and physical fitness are not enough to allow a man to go barging into airless voids or soundless speeds into which nature never intended him to trespass. There are so-called human restrictions over which physical man has little control. Such human restrictions mark the limits of man's ability to overcome physical stresses. So science has moved in and furnished, wherever possible, items contributing to safety and survival which allow man to explore beyond his own back yard.

A high-speed airplane often is subjected to moments of rather violent tumbling and buffeting motions. Although a pilot is held to the seat by safety belts, his head sometimes gets knocked against the hard glass or plastic of the cockpit canopy, or some other equally unyielding object. Due to this possibility, as well as the possibility of a crash landing or unsuccessful take-off, pilots are furnished with crash helmets. Usually these are plastic, insulated against shock and sound. They are equipped to accommodate

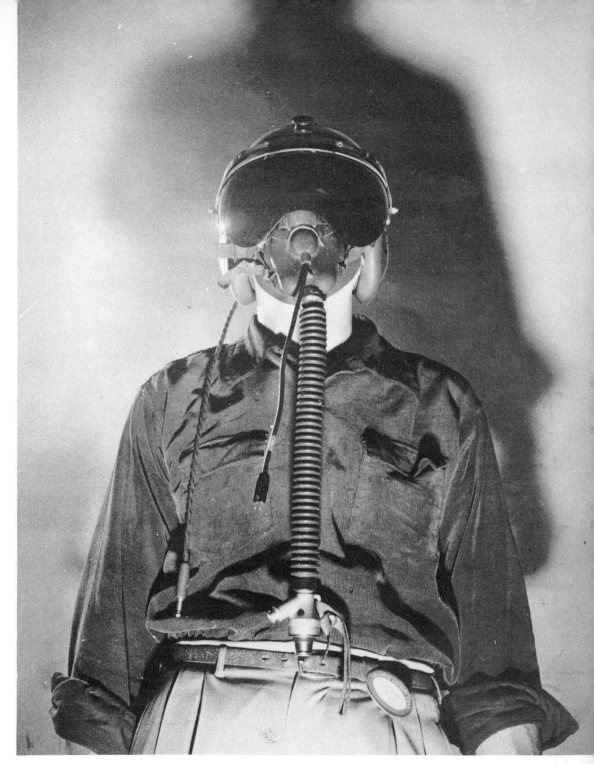

An improved headgear fashion for jet pilots includes a tinted visor for filtering out the blinding glare at high altitudes. Insulated crash helmet affords great protection. Radio and oxygen leads plug into the airplane's system.

radio earphones and oxygen masks and they look somewhat like oversized football helmets.

Since both jet and rocket aircraft operate best at high
altitudes, most of their flying is done well over the 20,000-
foot level. This, of course, makes it necessary for the pilot
to be fed oxygen in order to live. For this purpose he
wears a mask through which oxygen is furnished to him.
Attached to the mask is a piece of flexible tubing which
plugs into the oxygen-supply outlet. The oxygen tank is
usually attached to the airplane. However, many high-altitude fliers carry a small tank of oxygen strapped to their
bodies. If a pilot has to bail out from high up, the portable
supply will furnish life-sustaining oxygen until he has
parachuted to a lower altitude where there is breathable
air.

If a jet pilot's flight carries him over water, he usually
wears a Mae West inflatable vest. In case of an emergency
bail-out, the gas-filled rubber jacket will keep him afloat
until help arrives.

A much more complicated piece of flying clothing is
the G or anti-G suit. (G denotes the pull of gravity, 2G
twice the pull of gravity, etc.) The suits are sometimes
called Mach suits. (Mach 1 equals the speed of sound,
Mach 2.5 two and one-half times the speed of sound, etc.)
No matter by what name it is called, the G, anti-G, or
Mach pressure suit has but one purpose.

Speed itself has no harmful effect upon the human
body. Of course, a man must be protected from the wash

The U.S. Air Force T-1 high-altitude pressure suit enables pilots to survive in the near vacuum of the upper atmosphere.

of air which, at high speeds, could easily tear him apart if he were exposed to its blast. In aircraft, the enclosed cockpit protects the pilot from the brutal force of the wind, no matter what the speed of the airplane. The speed, in itself, is no hazard—not if the pilot starts slowly, keeps on a straight course, and does not "put on the brakes" too fast.

Danger results from the pilot's being exposed to rapid accelerations (quick speed-ups), sudden decelerations (quick slow-downs), or severe changes of direction. Being shot out of a cannon is a fair example of rapid acceleration. Crashing a bicycle into a stone wall would be a sure but rough method of learning about sudden deceleration. Speeding off the straightaway into the curve of a race track might illustrate a fairly moderate type of change of direction.

All of these three forms of movement are highly exaggerated in the field of aviation. The rapid acceleration of an airplane being catapulted from the deck of a ship presses the pilot against the back rest at about three times the force of gravity, or 3G. This creates three times the force that the human body was built to withstand comfortably.

A navy fighter plane landing on a carrier and being jerked to a quick stop by the arresting cables strung across the deck exerts upon the pilot approximately a similar 3G force. But because this is sudden deceleration, or stopping, the force is in the opposite or forward direction.

In either case, the blood tends to follow the direction of the gravity force. Since the force is in the opposite direction of the sudden movement, forward acceleration pushes the blood backward in the veins; a sudden stop pushes the blood forward. In either event, a part of the body is robbed of blood, while the other part is flooded with it.

A plus-G maneuver increases the downward or gravity pull on the body. Pulling out of a dive or banking into a high-speed turn are plus-G maneuvers. An elevator starting upward creates a very mild plus-G factor in the occupants.

The artificially increased gravity resulting from a sudden upward movement forces the blood downward away from the brain and heart and into the lower trunk and legs. Without the necessary life fluid, it takes only moments for the heart and brain to cease functioning properly. The pilot loses consciousness, or blacks out. If the plus-G pressure continues for any length of time, death will result.

A minus-G maneuver is one which tends to throw the body upward. Nosing over suddenly into a dive forces the pilot upward. If he were not held firmly by his safety belt he might well be catapulted right out through the top of the cockpit enclosure. Air pockets which cause an airplane to drop suddenly earthward create a minus-G condition. An elevator dropping toward the store basement is an everyday way of experiencing a mild and harmless minus-G maneuver.

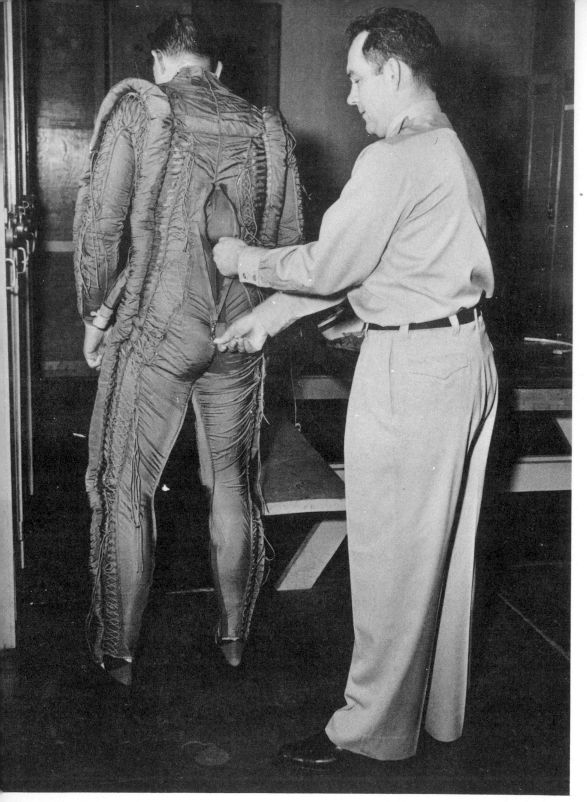

Getting into a snug T-1 pressure suit is definitely no one-man job.

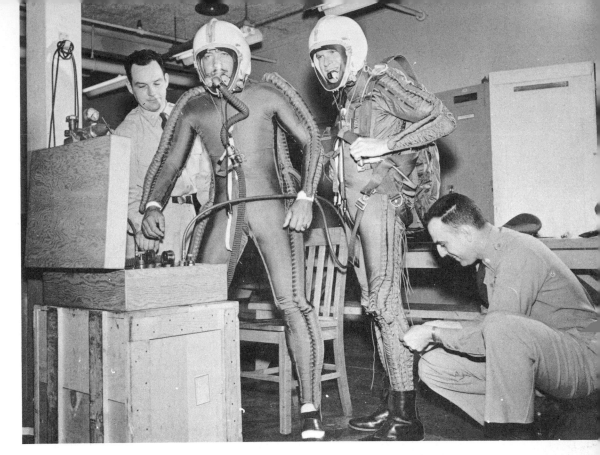

Inflating the tubular seams draws lacings and T-1 suit tight, preventing disastrous bloating which might result if pilot were subjected to the near-pressureless vacuum of the stratosphere.

A minus-G action of any great velocity forces the blood upward, flooding the brain, causing what is known as redding out. This flooding of the brain with blood can be even more dangerous than a plus-G condition, which robs the brain of blood. However, minus-G maneuvers of sufficient velocity and duration to red out the pilot are fairly rare. Thus, the purpose of the anti-G suit is mainly to prevent the much more common problem of increased gravity pull, or plus-G pull.

The function of the anti-G suit is as simple as it is essential. Atmospherically, a pressurized cabin usually protects the pilot. It maintains near sea-level pressures, even though he may be flying at an altitude of 60,000 feet. But there is always the frightening possibility of a pressure failure.

If the cockpit should ever spring a leak, the air in it would rush out, leaving nothing but a vacuum in the cockpit. If exposed to the pressureless vacuum, the very oxygen of the pilot's blood would bubble and boil. He would puff up and perish in a matter of seconds. To save him from a fatal lack of pressure, the anti-G suit is built to inflate automatically in such an emergency. The mechanical inflation of the tight suit squeezes the pilot's body together with a force similar to that exerted by the air near the ground. At the same time, a special pressurized helmet forces oxygen into the pilot's breathing passages, supercharging his lungs. The outside pressure of the constricting anti-G suit and the inside counterpressure of the oxygen protects the pilot from collapse and enables him to return safely "downstairs."

Add a parachute to the pilot's safety factors and he is carrying just about as much stuff as he can and still be able to climb into his airplane.

Such is the general protection for the high-flying jet pilot.

In 1953, the United States Navy released pictures of and a few facts (most details remain top secret) about the first real space suit. Like something from the pages of a Buck Rogers comic, this Navy pressure suit is deliberately

Already tested at altitudes of over 70,000 feet, the navy-developed space suit is an indication of man's protective needs for future interplanetary travel.

tailored for space travel. It is a one-piece affair made of rubberized fabric. It carries its own built-in atmosphere, which includes pressure, oxygen, and air-conditioning. A Martian-like transparent helmet hinges to the shoulders and seals in the suit's pressure when in place. The entire outfit can be worn for long periods of time. Despite its bulkiness and apparent clumsiness, the suit is built to allow the wearer complete freedom of movement.

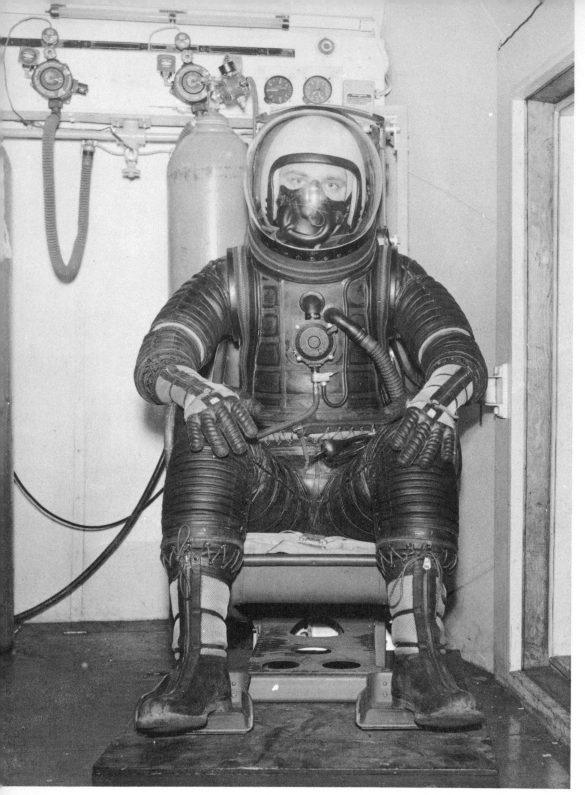

A flier rigged out in the U.S. Navy's new space suit. All details highly top-secret at present.

After exhaustive tests it was implied that the suit could be safely worn to the moon, provided there was a craft which could take a man there. Since the Navy is not given to making unfounded claims, we may assume that this suit, or later versions of it, might well be the solution to one problem encountered in exploring the unknown elements of outer space.

But a pilot does not pack all of his safety items on his person. The airplane manufacturers add their own contributions.

A jet engine radiates somewhere around 2500 degrees of temperature, Fahrenheit. This is a hot bonfire for a pilot either to be straddling or to have burning directly behind his back rest. In a rocket plane there is an even greater heat raging behind the pilot. Equally discomforting is the fact that large quantities of highly explosive jet or rocket propellants are contained in surrounding tanks.

So fire becomes a major hazard and a major concern to jet and rocket plane pilots. Wherever possible or practical, fire extinguishers are located at strategic spots in the airplane. In case of the superheated jet or rocket's causing a fire, the pilot cuts off the power and pulls a lever, and the entire internal mechanism is doused with extinguisher fluid or vapor.

But fire is not the only hazard. Nor, in the case of fire, does the pilot always have the opportunity to put it out and glide safely home.

Any number of emergencies can make it necessary for

a pilot to get away from the airplane as quickly and as far as possible. Since he invariably wears a parachute, this would seem to be no particular problem. However, bailing out of a modern high-speed airplane is not the simple function it used to be in the planes of the past. Ultra speed and high altitude are both very real deterrents to safe escape. At speeds in excess of 300 miles per hour, which is very slow for jets, a pilot leaving the cockpit of a crippled plane could jump neither far enough nor fast enough to clear the rear rudder fin or horizontal stabilizer. At faster speeds the rush of wind upon the pilot attempting to bail out would be fatal.

At the extremely high altitudes haunted only by jet and rocket craft there must be added the problem of survival in an oxygenless atmosphere having a temperature of around 65 degrees below zero.

Two safety devices, the ejection seat and the jettisonable cockpit, are the present answers to these problems.

Most combat-type aircraft employ some form of ejection seat. If it becomes necessary for a pilot to abandon his airplane in a hurry, he unlatches the transparent plastic canopy over his head and lets it fly away into the wind stream. Then he jerks a lever, which explodes a powder charge. The entire seat, with him still in it, is shot upward with sufficient bone-jarring velocity to clear the projecting tail surfaces. Once well away from the airplane, the pilot unbuckles his safety belt and lets the seat drop free. Then he pulls the ripcord, feels the jerk of the chute blossoming out overhead, and floats to earth in normal parachute fashion. If he is at an extremely high altitude when the emergency occurs he will, of course, hook his oxygen hose to his own portable tank before pulling the ejection-seat lever.

In order to escape the cold he may wisely allow himself to free-fall a few thousand feet while still strapped to the ejection seat. When he has reached a lower and safer altitude, he will let the seat drop free, pull his ripcord, and parachute the remainder of the distance to the ground.

If all this sounds simple, it is not. But pilots, courageous men to begin with, undergo rigorous training schedules which develop complete emotional and muscular control— a combination which can get almost anyone out of a jam, no matter how critical it may seem.

So the ejection seat has proved to be a valuable safety factor for the pilots of subsonic aircraft. Sometimes a subsonic airplane approaches the speed of sound. If he has time to do it, a pilot will pull every flap control and slow down the plane as much as possible before he jerks the ejection seat lever that will catapult him out into the punishing wind stream.

If the airplane is of the transonic or supersonic class, the ejection seat does not ensure a pilot's safety in abandoning a burning or otherwise crippled ship. At any speed even remotely approaching that of sound, he must have a more complete protection from the death-dealing blow of the wind. Besides, a pilot forced to bail out at extreme

An experimental, fully insulated and pressurized jettisonable cockpit is subjected to rigorous test-track trials. A rocket charge explodes it forward at a speed approaching that of sound and comparable to the force with which it might be propelled away from a stricken aircraft.

altitudes must be protected from exposure to the cold and pressureless vacuum of space.

The jettisonable cockpit answers this survival problem for superspeed and upper-atmosphere aircraft. Here again it is a case of pulling that last-chance lever. This time not only the seat, but the entire cockpit explodes away from the plane.

This might be just the nose shell, inside of which the pilot huddles in his pressurized suit until he reaches a slow enough falling speed, in the lower altitudes, so that he

162

Its downward fall checked by a series of parachutes, the sealed capsule of the jettisonable cockpit can drop safely on water or land.

may safely resort to his parachute. Then again, it may be the entire pressurized cabin, pilot and all, which explodes out into space and floats safely to the ground with the help of automatically released parachutes. Many variations of the jettisonable cabin are in drawing-board stages, or are being tested, or are already in use.

But whatever variation of the ejection seat or jettisonable cabin is incorporated into a plane, it is there for one purpose and one only—as is true of all the other pilot-safety devices. All of them are there for the single purpose

163

of protecting that scant two dollars' worth of chemical elements put together into a priceless package of courage and ability—the man who flies the airplane.

8

BUILT FOR SPEED

LATE in 1945 several naval officers and members of the National Advisory Committee for Aeronautics (NACA) sat with a small group of aircraft designers and engineers in Los Angeles, California. The scene of the meeting was an office of one of the world's largest manufacturers of both commercial and military aircraft.

In brief, the visiting bigwigs wanted to know if these men were ready to tackle the building of the airplane of tomorrow.

They were. In fact, they had spent months working out their ideas of what the supersonic airplanes of tomorrow would be like. They had stacks of drawings and reams of data on the dream aircraft. Now they were being asked to go to work and convert their ideas into something that would fly.

Mr. Ed Heinemann, the tall, energetic chief engineer

of Douglas Aircraft's El Segundo Division brought out the sketches and figures. He spread them out in front of the visitors, who gave them a thorough going over.

"This might be it and it might not," they said noncommittally. "You see, all we really want is an airplane that will do two things. It must fly faster and it must fly higher than any airplane ever has flown before. And, unlike the neat job that Bell Aircraft Corporation is building for the Air Force, we want your airplane to be capable of taking off and landing on its own power. You know—just like any ordinary airplane." The speaker smiled.

This was quite an order to fill. The engineers had heard of the Bell X-1 project. They had guessed that the X-1's goal was to pierce that still mysterious and dangerously threatening invisible wall of sound. Strictly rocket-powered, with a very short duration of flight, the X-1, it was rumored, was to be launched at a high altitude from a mother ship. After making a quick, spurting attempt to slice through the sonic barrier, the X-1 would glide back to earth on a dead stick. It was further hoped that in doing all this the X-1 would remain in one piece.

Actually, what the visitors seemed to want now was an airplane that would take off, land, and do everything any ordinary combat plane would do—yet go faster and even higher than the man-carrying rocket missile known as the X-1.

The engineers knew pretty well the reason for the request for a high-speed research aircraft. Combat fliers had reported strange reactions of the controls when a power-diving fighter approached Mach 1 (speed of sound).

Sometimes the controls would become stiff and sluggish. A pilot had to exert every ounce of his strength in order to pull out of a dive. At other times the airplane would start to tuck under, as though to start a fatal outside loop. Again the pilot would have to bring full wit and strength into play in order to bring the plane out of the dive. Many believed that the controls actually froze tight when the plane reached a speed approaching that of sound. And since in the military aircraft of those days this speed could be reached only during a power dive, it was believed that this freezing of the controls was the tragic reason why some planes never pulled out of their dives.

But these were only a few of the many problems which the new airplane must tackle. There were many others—both known and unknown.

"Well," one of the men prompted, "what do you say?"

The chief engineer looked at the group of co-workers gathered around him. They had been working together for years. They had figured out many an airplane together. They had given their flying craft birth on paper. They had watched them grow into finished products of aluminum, plastic, steel, and the hundred-odd other materials which go into making an airplane. They had seen them fly off to every corner of the globe to do both peacetime and wartime duty.

During the years, these men had become a team, a real

Traveling at around 100 miles per hour when passing through this section of NACA's transonic wind tunnel, the air is later squeezed down and the speed increased to over 700 miles per hour by the time it reaches the test cell.

team working together for victory over the hazards of the skies. To them this was just another challenge, although a much greater one than they had ever met before.

Mr. Heinemann looked around at his team. He liked the eagerness on their faces and the sharp gleam in their eyes. "We'll do it," he said simply.

But the next year was not so simple. In order to design and construct a supersonic aircraft, it seemed that both engineers and builders had to throw away a lot of ideas they had learned in past years.

A full-sized F-86 Sabre fighter is mounted in the enormous test section
of the world's largest wind tunnel at Ames Aeronautical Laboratory in
California.

Usually they had been able to work with wind tunnels. They had been able to put full-sized aircraft through wind-tunnel tests. In most cases they had their answers to various problems before the real airplane was sent into the skies. But when it came to supersonic craft, wind tunnels posed a problem. The only wind tunnels available at that time which could fan up a breeze blowing faster than sound were not large enough to handle anything but small model planes. And such models could not accommodate enough instruments or furnish really accurate readings of stresses and strains. In other words, they could not furnish the necessary answers to the real questions of supersonic flying. They could give hints—often quite accurate hints—but that was about all. Another answer had to be sought.

"What's wrong with using nature's wind tunnel?" someone proposed. Then he added, smiling, "And it's plenty big enough to hold anything we can send up there."

So without the advantage of knowing how things were going to react once the airplane was in the air, the men consulted their slide rules, crossed their fingers, and went about finishing the first of the Douglas-built airplanes to attempt shattering the sonic barrier.

This airplane was the D-558, Skystreak. Built for lightness, yet loaded with an enormous array of instruments, the Skystreak tipped the scales at nearly 10,000 pounds fully loaded. For this weight, no single pound of which was not absolutely essential, the Skystreak had a ridicu-

A scale model of the D-558-2 Skyrocket undergoes tests in a wind tunnel at Langley Aeronautical Laboratory, Hampton, Va. The wind tunnel aids in determining whether the airplane can withstand rolls, spins, and other erratic maneuvers.

lously small and stubby wing. It spanned a scant 25 feet from tip to tip. The fuselage was 35 feet long. Unless you could see inside the cigar-shaped body, you would wonder—and rightly so—how such a small wing area could support such a heavy airplane in flight.

Of course, the answer was inside—a General Electric TG-180 turbojet power plant. It occupied most of the fuselage behind the pilot's cockpit. In fact, the pilot was required to straddle the two tunnel-like ducts which carried the air from the twin intakes in the nose back into the engine's compressor. This turbojet engine was capable of kicking out over 4000 pounds of thrust, roughly the

171

full horsepower of 75 average modern automobiles. Although at the time this was a big engine, later jets were built to produce over two and one half times that amount of power.

The Skystreak itself was made primarily of aluminum alloy and lighter, yet tougher, magnesium alloy. It had a tricycle landing gear. Its pilot's compartment was pressurized and contained both heating and refrigerating mechanism. Since there was no telling the strains the airplane might be subjected to when it began nudging the sonic wall, the Skystreak was built to withstand 18G, or eighteen times the pull of gravity.

The Skystreak carried over 500 pounds of gauges and electronic instruments. Their purpose was to record every strain, flutter, sway, and impulse that the Skystreak might encounter in its effort to penetrate the so-called sonic wall.

The Skystreak took to the air a year and a half after its first sketchy appearance on the engineers' scratch pads. Since red markings are the accepted color to denote research aircraft, the builders of the Skystreak painted the airplane a brilliant crimson from wing tip to wing tip, from air intake to tail pipe. In truth, it appeared to be a streak of fire darting through the sky; hence Skystreak was a very fitting name.

After a couple of months of shakedown flights aimed at ironing out a few of the bugs, the Skystreak was ready for advanced tests.

On the morning of August 20, 1947, Commander

BUILT FOR SPEED

Turner F. Caldwell, Jr., of the United States Navy, climbed into the Skystreak and took off from the dry lake bed near the desert flight base of Muroc, California. The name of the testing center was later officially established as Edwards Air Force Base. Commander Caldwell took a couple of practice runs along the measured course, then opened the throttle as far as it would go.

The carefully laid out course measured an exact 3 kilometers (1.863 miles). The commander took four low altitude passes over it. To equalize such factors as tail winds, head winds, or any others which might affect the flight in a single direction, rulings require that a flier make two runs in each direction over the course. The official speed is the average speed of the four runs.

After sixteen minutes in the air the young Navy officer set the Skystreak down again on the desert floor. He was figuratively clutching a new world's speed record of 640.7 miles per hour—17 miles an hour faster than the record existing at the time. But the Annapolis-trained flier was allowed to hold onto his new record for only a few short days—four to be exact.

On August 25, as noon approached and 90-degree heat waves shimmered across the desert flats, Major Marion E. Carl, United States Marines, squeezed his six-foot-two-inch gaunt frame into the already crowded cockpit of the Skystreak. Experienced in thrust flying, Major Carl had been the first pilot to land a jet airplane aboard an aircraft carrier.

The official speed-course site on the Mojave Desert is located in a great amphitheater ringed by rugged ranges of mountains. The parched desert earth is speckled with low clumps of cactus, sage, and mesquite. Joshua trees cast grotesque shadows across the beige-colored sand. But there are no bushes or foliage of any kind on the barren twelve-mile-long clay bed of the ancient dry lake. This flat, smooth landing field built by nature stretches for miles in all directions.

The speed course is marked off near one edge of the vast expanse. A broad black guide line, along which the pilot can aim his aircraft, stretches straight down the center of the course. Colored smoke flares located beyond each end of the measured strip serve as additional guide beacons. Electronically controlled precision cameras record the start and finish and compute the elapsed time it takes an aircraft to move between them. These cameras are operated from a single control tower off to one side.

In order to keep the Skystreak from starting its run too high and taking advantage of the speed acquired from a steep dive, the maximum starting altitude at Muroc is 1310 feet. Two droning aircraft patrol overhead at that height. The speed pilot must start his run below their level.

Watching one of these speed runs from the ground has its own brand of thrills. Since Major Carl was last seen heading westward, we keep our eyes on a spot above the distant mountain range. A faint smudge of brownish

Displayed on the wing are instruments which record every quiver, flutter, sway, or impulse of a supersonic high-altitude research airplane such as the Douglas Skyrocket or the Bell X-1 (shown here).

smoke appears, becoming more and more definite as we watch. In front of it, and growing rapidly, is the Skystreak, flying below the maximum altitude of 1310 feet.

Suddenly the Skystreak eases into a gentle slanting dive toward the narrow lane of the sprint course. An eerie hush precedes the amazingly rapid arrival of the growing speck. Like a red dart trailing a feather of flame, the Skystreak blazes down low across the short course and, in a twinkling, is past and growing small in the opposite direction. Seemingly seconds later, the throaty roar of its jet exhaust thunders across the field. But the Skystreak has already started into its flat figure-eight turn in preparation for the next run from the opposite direction.

On that 25th of August, Major Carl, by the time he had made his four runs over the measured course, was holder of a new official world's speed record of 650.7 miles per hour.

Further tests proved that this was just about the limit to the speed that could be coaxed out of the jet-powered Skystreak. It was believed at that time that this was fast enough for all practical purposes, although today that speed is reached and surpassed by many regular production-line aircraft—a fine testimonial to the amazing advancement of jet aviation in America. The Skystreak, with its horde of instruments, had furnished the aircraft industry an enormous amount of valuable information, which aided this advancement immeasurably.

But the normal design of the airplane and the limited power available from the single turbojet engine just did not seem to be the right combination to get the Skystreak out of subsonic range and deeper into the transonic range, that area of compressibility and sonic turbulence which was of greatest concern to airmen and engineers alike.

Yet the builders of the Skystreak were well prepared for its limitations. They had assumed after early tests that the Skystreak, although a very worthy and valuable flying laboratory, might not solve the problem of supersonic flight. There was also the subject of altitude, which was becoming of increasing interest to a suddenly space-minded public. The Skystreak, with its turbojet engine which consumed vast quantities of atmospheric oxygen, could not operate in the stratosphere, where oxygen in any quantity is nonexistent.

So during the time when the Skystreak was making its tests and breaking speed records, another project was under way at the Douglas Aircraft Company's El Segundo Plant near Los Angeles. In fact, the planning and construction of the experimental Skyrocket came so close upon the heels of the Skystreak that the two can be considered one continuous project. The D-558-2, Skyrocket, had the advantage of the many findings which emerged from the numerous test flights of her elder sister, the Skystreak.

Then, just before the Skyrocket was ready to be flown, the aviation world—in fact, the public in general—were excited by a long-awaited announcement. With Major Charles (Chuck) Yeager at the controls, the Bell X-1 had, for the first time in aviation history, pierced the wall of sound. The history-making event occurred on October 14, 1947.

Yet there was a difference between the Bell X-1 and the Douglas D-558 projects. The X-1 had been built strictly for the purpose of carrying a man through the sonic barrier. Its wing was machined from a solid piece of aluminum alloy instead of being built in the usual rib-and-brace manner of normal aircraft. The fat, needle-nosed, and highly streamlined fuselage contained a four-rocket motor capable of creating 12,000 horsepower's worth of thrust at extreme altitudes. Even though all available space was given over to fuel tanks, the X-1 was capable of staying aloft at full throttle only for about two and a half minutes.

Unable to take off on its own power, the X-1 was carried aloft to a 30,000-foot altitude in the belly of a mother ship, a B-29 bomber with a specially fitted bomb bay. After being cut loose, the X-1 had streaked away to win the honor of being the first piloted aircraft ever to exceed the speed of sound. Years later its speed was announced as 967 miles per hour.

Shortly thereafter, the Douglas D-558-2, Skyrocket, was taken out of wraps. A longer and much thinner airplane than the X-1, the Skyrocket has a slightly shorter wing span. The wings and tail are sharply swept back, giving an illusion of speed even when the airplane is parked quietly on the ramp.

Like the Skystreak, the Skyrocket was first equipped with a turbojet engine, enabling it to take off, fly, and land under its own power. But in addition to the J-34 turbojet engine built by Westinghouse, the Skyrocket also carried a four-tube rocket motor similar to the one used in the X-1. Reaction Motors, Inc., America's leading manufacturer of rocket engines, had built the motors specifically for use in the research airplanes. Each of the four rocket tubes is capable of generating 1500 pounds of thrust, or a combined full-power output of 6000 pounds.

BUILT FOR SPEED

In the arrangement of the power plants and fuel systems great care was taken to distribute all fuel uniformly about the airplane's center of gravity. Unless carefully planned and corrected, the shift of weight caused by rapidly emptying fuel tanks can raise havoc with any aircraft, tipping it off balance one way or another. The usual correction for this shift of weight is accomplished by trimming the controls. If the fuel is used up in the forward tanks first, the full rear tanks cause the airplane to become tail-heavy. To compensate for this tendency to sag at the tail, the trim tabs are cranked to a position where they will bring the tail back up to normal flight condition. Trim tabs are small control surfaces similar to horizontal stabilizers, or ailerons. Instead of being obliged to keep moving his stick or rudder pedals to compensate for the airplane's tendency to be thrown off balance by changing distributions of weight, the pilot can rely on the trim tabs to correct the fault and keep the aircraft flying a level course. Trim tabs often require frequent adjusting.

But in a fast-speed plane such as the Skyrocket, finding the proper amount of trim in such a short time and keeping it correct as the fuel is rapidly consumed can become quite a hazard; the pilot is too busy with other things. So the problem of shifting weight is best solved by a proper distribution of fuel, which allows it to be drained evenly into the engine without throwing the airplane off its center of gravity.

The jet-exhaust outlets are also carefully aimed to direct the thrust through the center of gravity and thus minimize the necessity of trimming against an off-balance thrust. As can be seen, trimming an airplane serves the same purpose as jockeying the tiller of a sailboat—to keep the craft on a straight and even course, no matter what pressures of wind or shifting weight tend to make it veer off from its true direction.

The Skyrocket carried 250 gallons of aviation gasoline for its turbojet engine. In addition there were special tanks of highly explosive rocket fuel and oxidizer.

Magnesium alloy, light and extremely strong, covers the greater portion of the Skyrocket's fuselage. The wing and tail surfaces are made largely of aluminum alloy.

The short, sharply swept-back wing has very little surface area. This, of course, offers poor low-speed lifting power. Automatic Handley-Page slots are placed in the leading edge of the wing. When they open out they produce additional lift, making slower and safer landing speeds possible. During flight the slots are retracted into the wing.

Since the small thin wing is incapable of housing the landing gear, the wheel wells are cut into the fuselage.

As an added factor for controlling drag or speed, aerodynamic brakes are built into each side of the fuselage. These are simply doorlike rectangles which fold into the fuselage back near the tail. When the pilot wants to reduce speed preparatory to coming in for a landing, he flicks the proper switch and the doors are shoved out hydraulically.

Various shapes are rocketed into the sky and electronically tracked in order to study aerodynamic resistance of the atmosphere and the effects of streamlining.

Poking out into the air stream, they can quickly slow down the plane's speed. In fact, similar dive brakes have been built into various military aircraft. Of course, a pilot throttles back before he opens out the dive brakes. Otherwise, the high-speed slip stream might tear off the entire rear fuselage.

The Skyrocket's cockpit, like that of the Skystreak, is pressurized and equipped with refrigeration and heating. The refrigeration unit itself is a neat little package weighing a slight 16 pounds, but it is capable of producing an amount of cold air equivalent to the output of 40 average home refrigerators. This refrigeration system becomes a very handy item to have around. At 800 miles an hour, the friction heat generated by the air brushing against the outside of the airplane increases the temperature by about 145 degrees, Fahrenheit. At 1000 miles per hour, even in the cold rarefied atmosphere of high altitudes, the increase is over 200 degrees, enough to roast an unprotected pilot in short order.

The Skyrocket carries over 600 pounds of various types and sizes of instruments. Supplementing the standard cockpit panel instruments—altimeters, air-speed indicators, artificial horizons, various other gauges—there are about four miles of strain-gauge wiring and three miles of pressure tubing woven throughout the wings and fuselage of the small craft.

Readings from over 400 air-pressure-measuring points, 900 electric-impulse strain gauges, and the data produced by many other flight-factor instruments provide the material for the log of each flight. Since the pilot has enough to do without worrying about all this detail, the special instruments are located behind the cockpit, where automatic cameras make permanent film records of what happens during each flight. In truth, the Skyrocket is a flying test tube.

All in all, this is the picture of the D-558-2, Skyrocket, a worthy representative in the select field of research aircraft, which also includes the Bell X-1 (now proudly retired to the air museum of the Smithsonian Institution), Bell's X-1A, X-2, and X-5, Douglas Aircraft's X-3, Northrop's X-4 (also retired), and—possibly—other models being built or tested under absolute secrecy.

All of these research aircraft, affectionately called flying test tubes, vary greatly in design. But all are built and flown for a common purpose: to increase man's knowledge and so extend his operations deeper into the ever-receding frontiers of ultrasonic speed and high-altitude flight.

9

JUST TESTING

THE slow and deliberate process of testing a research airplane in the fields of supersonic and stratospheric flight certainly is not without danger and excitement. The case of the Douglas Skyrocket is fairly typical of what happens with any research aircraft once it is ready to take the air.

The first person to start taking the bugs out of any research airplane is quite likely to be the aircraft company's chief test pilot. His purpose is not to push the craft to its maximum speed or altitude. He takes upon himself the job of determining whether the heavy, small-winged airplane will fly at all. For, even though on paper and as indicated by wind-tunnel tests with small models the craft will surely fly, the only real proof of the pudding is to put the full-sized airplane into the sky.

In the case of the Skyrocket, not only did it have to fly, it had to take off, land, and otherwise conduct itself like

The Skyrocket has its own portable "hangar," equipped to service, fuel, repair, or transport the test craft whenever and wherever needed.

any other normal aircraft. For, after all, the D-558-2 was not conceived simply as a man-carrying projectile. It was designed and built as a test craft and as a possible fore-runner of later models of military and, in the more distant future, even commercial airplanes.

The first pilot to test the plane had little difficulty getting the airworthy Skyrocket aloft. However, he soon found that the sleek needle-nosed craft became dangerously unstable at certain high subsonic speeds. He made numerous test flights in an effort to determine the cause. Each flight was followed by various corrections and me-

186

chanical adjustments. Finally satisfied that the Skyrocket was ready for advanced tests, the chief pilot turned the combination jet and rocket airplane over to another veteran test pilot.

This second pilot's work with the earlier Skystreak had furnished much valuable data and had established him as one of the few men considered capable of handling the even hotter Skyrocket.

But it was not this man's job to start out breaking records. As a matter of fact, the Skyrocket was not intended to be a record-breaking airplane. Like the crimson Skystreak, it was built to act as a flying laboratory so that engineers and aerodynamicists could study a full-sized aircraft's reactions to high speeds and high altitudes. As mentioned earlier, the Skyrocket, from the needle nose to the rocket-tube exhausts, is a maze of wires, tubing, and myriad delicate instruments which record, electronically or mechanically, the airplane's every slight reaction to the stresses and strains of flight.

Yet despite the most innocent intentions, the Skyrocket was destined to break records. The test pilot began by climbing up to thirty or forty thousand feet on jet power. Then, in the thin sub-zero atmosphere, he would level off for straight flight, cut in the rockets, and let her go.

One day, after several weeks of preliminary tests, the pilot opened all throttles wide. The airplane, a flame-trailing white sliver of aluminum and magnesium alloys, streaked through the desert sky to become the first airplane capable of taking off and landing on its own power to exceed the speed of sound. (The Bell X-1, remember, had been launched high in the air from the belly of a B-29 mother ship).

The old bromide about the rest of the olives being easy to get out of the jar once you have removed the first one held true of the Skyrocket. In no time at all, it became routine for it to charge through the sonic barrier. But this was possible only by using the rockets in addition to the jet engine. Since the enormous turbojet occupied so much of the Skyrocket's interior space, there was room left for only a small amount of rocket fuel. So no sooner did the airplane get through the wall of sound than the rockets reached burnout and the pilot had to head back toward the field.

With each flight the Skyrocket was brought down lower and lower to the "deck." Thus far all the supersonic flights of both the Bell X-1 and the Skyrocket had been made high up in the cold top reaches of the troposphere. It was feared that down low in the thick, warm air, the gremlins which had frozen the controls of combat aircraft and caused others to disintegrate or to tuck under in tragic dives might appear again.

The test pilot was willing to find out. One morning, with the first red of the rising sun just appearing over the eastern foothills which edge the desert, he walked out to the waiting airplane. He was dressed in ordinary street clothes, open collar and all. There would be no need for pressure suits or electrically heated clothes that day. He would be down low. If anything bothered him, it probably would be the heat, though the cockpit refrigeration should keep him from being toasted by friction heat. He wore a bright crimson crash helmet, and a parachute dangled from his hips.

As usual, the ground crew had been working since midnight getting the Skyrocket in top flight condition. "Everything's in order," the ground-crew chief assured the pilot. "If you find anything that doesn't work, you just bring it back and we'll give you a new one."

The flier laughed lightly at the crewman's somewhat grisly joke. When something fails at supersonic speeds, the pilot does not often get an opportunity to exchange it for a new one. But he was not worried. Those fellows on the ground crew knew the Skyrocket from abacus to zebra and babied her with more care than a mother bear with a single cub.

Once again the speed course had been marked off. The electric cameras were set to record the start and finish and the time that was spent in between. Most of the engineers who had planned and built the test craft were on hand. The tension on their faces showed that they were obviously anxious and possibly a little worried about this first attempt to assault the sonic barrier right down near the ground. Down low, if anything went wrong, there was little chance of bailing out or otherwise correcting the danger—little chance, in fact, of ever knowing what had gone wrong.

Gene May, veteran test pilot, stands by the four barrels of the Skyrocket's powerful rocket engine.

JUST TESTING

After talking over his flight plans with the crewmen and engineers on the ground, the pilot climbed into the Skyrocket and fastened the airtight cockpit canopy down over his head. He knew pretty well how a caterpillar must feel in its cocoon.

The hard-packed clay of the dry lake stretched out for miles ahead of him. It was a comforting thought to have such a nice long runway from which to take off. Heavily loaded with her capacity of both jet and rocket fuels, the Skyrocket would need a great deal of that distance to get off the ground.

At the all-clear signal from the control tower, the test pilot eased forward on the jet throttle. The giant turbine wailed like a wounded banshee. The Skyrocket trundled forward, slowly picking up speed. Finally she was clocking a hundred miles an hour . . . 125 . . . 150 . . . 160. One mile . . . two . . . three miles passed beneath the small, spinning wheels. Yet the heavily laden and small-winged Skyrocket refused to budge off the smooth landing strip.

Beads of sweat began to form on the pilot's forehead. Would she ever lift off? Then he remembered one little trick that might get her into the air. He had thought of trying it on other occasions, but had never been forced to do it. Now, as the jagged hills at the end of the runway seemed to be racing angrily toward him, he reached for the rocket switch. In quick succession, he fired two of the four rocket tubes. The sudden surge of extra thrust pressed him hard into the back rest as the rockets took hold. The throaty roar of the exhaust boomed loudly inside the cockpit. The pilot tugged on the semi-wheel of the steering yoke. The Skyrocket protested with a shudder, then heeded the persistent pressure of the hand on the controls, and lifted gently into the air. Quickly the pilot retracted the landing wheels. After 20 seconds he switched off the rockets; he would need his rocket propellant for the speed run. Besides, the Skyrocket was air-borne and the jet would keep her aloft.

A few minutes later the plane whistled down out of the sky in a long, slanting approach toward the marked-off course. Snapping on his radio, the test flier called the tower for a smoke bomb. At supersonic speed, which he hoped to reach that day, he would need more than the guide lines on the ground to keep him on his course. Columns of rising smoke at each end of the course would make good targets at which to aim the Skyrocket's needle nose.

Far up ahead two puffs of orange smoke billowed into the air. The pilot made a quick last-minute check of the cockpit. Everything seemed in order. The Skyrocket was doing about 650 miles per hour, pressing lower and lower to the ground. The Mojave Desert was a cactus-studded carpet stretching ahead, blurring out as it came closer.

The pilot pressed the microphone button again. "Muroc Tower, Navy 973 coming in on final twenty miles. Ready to fire rockets. Here they go! Rocket Number One . . . Rocket Number Two . . . Number Three . . . Four!"

Even as he talked into the mike, the pilot's hand was

flicking the switches. He felt the giant thrust of each added rocket tube smash the plane forward, pressing him harder into the back rest. The lake bed came rushing to meet him. Dropping still lower, he kept his eyes and thoughts ten miles out ahead of his flight. He had to think far ahead. At that speed, by the time he might focus his eyes or mind on what was beneath or to either side of him he would be far past it.

Suddenly the Skyrocket began to rumble and shake. It was like driving a flat-tired truck over a rough cobblestone road. This was the shock-wave turbulence of the transonic speed range. The airplane was racing its own sound. The compressed air and the sound waves building up and tearing away from the wings in chunks proved that the sonic barrier had been reached.

The aircraft's controls grew sluggish. It felt somewhat as though the plane were flying through thick syrup. But at that high speed and low altitude the pilot had no desire to move the controls quickly. Fortunately, the Skyrocket showed no tendency to tuck under and dive, a maneuver which would have been immediately fatal at that altitude.

Then, with startling suddenness, the throaty roar of the rockets was no longer present. It had dropped far off to the rear somewhere. A surge of exhilaration swept through the pilot. He realized that he was zipping along faster than the speed of sound. The turbulence was gone, and he was flying in the glassy slick air of that world beyond the speed of sound—the supersonic.

An extra thrill was added to his achievement by the knowledge that he had proved once and for all that, no matter how high or how low the craft may fly, there is no such thing as a solid sonic barrier capable of tearing a well-constructed airplane apart. There may be violent turbulence at times, and there may be strange reactions from the controls. But there is no obstacle resistant enough to prevent an airplane from breaking through it and going on into the quiet world of supersonic speeds.

But the elated flier did not have much time or desire to daydream about the flight. He had traveled the marked-off five-mile course in less than a half minute. Counting the take-off and speed approach, the rockets had been on full power for less than two minutes. Yet in that short period of time they had consumed nearly two tons of fuel and oxidizer. The pilot was beginning to perspire freely now, but he realized thankfully that the cockpit refrigeration was working. If it were not, the friction heat on the Skyrocket's outside skin would probably be seeping in to cook him like an ear of corn in its husk. Even with the insulation and refrigeration, some of that heat was soaking through into the cockpit.

There was no cause for worry, however. The last of the rocket propellant was coughing through the tubes. The Skyrocket slowed down, passing quickly back through the area of turbulence caused by its own sound waves and into the smoother subsonic zone. Switching off the rockets, the pilot pulled back on the steering yoke in order to gain altitude before coming in for a landing on jet power.

He called the tower for landing clearance and got it. He lowered his landing wheels, opened the slots in the leading edges of the wing, and tripped the lever which opened out the doorlike dive brakes on each side of the fuselage. Even with all of this speed-slowing help, the Sky-rocket touched down on the desert floor at a whizzing 170 miles an hour.

Another successful flight through sound had been accomplished. When all the readings and filmed data were taken from the maze of automatic recording instruments packed into the Skyrocket, the entire aircraft industry stood to profit by the results . . . and did.

Once the so-called sonic barrier had been broken, aviation advanced in amazing strides. Since interest seemed to be directed toward climbing ever higher into the sky, where the air was less turbulent and its thinness allowed faster and smoother flying, aeronautical research began focusing its attention on the stratosphere . . . and beyond.

10

ALL SET FOR A BIG ONE

SINCE research aircraft were soon operating mostly in the stratosphere, where there is insufficient oxygen to support combustion, jet engines were eliminated and the planes were converted entirely to rocket power.

There are many additional factors to consider in planning, building, and flying a man-carrying research vehicle aimed at ever increasing ultrasonic speeds in the highest reaches of the atmosphere.

At supersonic speeds the friction heat created by the brushing air stream caused the tempered-plastic portholes through which a pilot looked to bubble and start to melt. Thick plate glass capable of withstanding a much higher degree of heat was quickly substituted.

Painting a supersonic airplane is a highly specialized process, very different from the practice of daubing a coat or two of enamel upon an automobile fender. The strains

197

of high-speed turns cause even the best of finishes to check and crack. The sub-zero cold of high altitudes, the contrasting friction heat of speed runs, the peppering of minute dust particles, and the corrosion from rocket chemicals all raise havoc with a paint job.

Special mixes of highly resistant lacquer are used to overcome, as well as possible, the many hazards of supersonic and high-altitude test flying. Each paint job requires about twenty coats of this lacquer. Each coat is carefully pumiced down by hand rubbing. A high polish is added to the final coat, making the research aircraft slick as a greased eel and cutting down the possibility of the air's grabbing hold and creating friction heat.

Some research aircraft manufactures prefer the slick surface of the unpainted aluminum-alloy skin and only fill the minute pores of the metal with the substance of the polish. The unpainted Bell X-1A has flown to new records of speed.

A rocket motor is notoriously thirsty. Carrying sufficient fuel to keep it operating for any prolonged period of time is a major problem. The size of today's ultrasonic research planes limits the fuel capacity to about 4 tons. (Rocket fuels are measured in pounds rather than gallons. Since their density varies with the changing pressures encountered at high altitude, a gallon gauge would not give an accurate reading.) Although 8000 pounds of fuel seems a lot—and is—it is actually very little when one considers that the combined fuel consumption of the four tubes of a rocket motor is over a ton a minute. Obviously four minutes' worth of fuel is not enough to take a rocket plane from the ground to the stratosphere and still have enough left to explore new speed frontiers or high-altitude barriers.

The original Bell X-1 solved that problem, and the solution used by the X-1 has been used in all high-flying and ultrasonic speed tests ever since.

It is a simple matter of inverted pickaback riding. A Boeing B-29 heavy bomber is modified to fit the need. Its bomb bay is enlarged and reshaped to carry the smaller research craft instead of a bomb. Snuggled tightly up against the underside of this mother ship, the research airplane can be carried part way up into the sky. Then, when the heavily loaded B-29 reaches the maximum altitude to which it can climb, it releases the research craft. With its fuel tanks still fully loaded, the rocket craft . . . But perhaps the best way to get the actual feel of it is to take a flight yourself.

So for the next few minutes why don't you step into the exciting role of a test pilot? Your assignment is to sit at the controls and fly one of today's rocket-powered research airplanes on a supersonic flight into the upper reaches of the sky.

You will be wise to talk things over first with a few members of the ever-growing elite corps of supersonic fliers. They can familiarize you with many of the hurdles you must be capable of clearing if your assault on the sonic barrier or your attempt to scale to new and dangerous

During the dark hours before dawn, the Skyrocket has been carefully
serviced and checked.

heights is to be successful. They will be willing, even
eager, to furnish you with any knowledge they have gained.
There is no selfishness among pilots. Friendly competition, yes; selfishness, no. Whether they have flown in the
D-558-2, the X-1A, X-2, X-3, or any of the other research
craft, their efforts have been toward a common purpose—
to extend man's over-all knowledge of the skies and promote the discovery of the eventual trail into space.

After spending numerous hours acquainting yourself
with the airplane, the crew who services it, and the work

The B-29 mother ship is hoisted on stilts so that the Skyrocket can snuggle into her specially built bomb bay.

of the large and varied group of technicians involved in the flying project, you feel that you are all set for a big one. The meteorologist connected with the project picks a bright summer morning for you to make your flight. Conditions aloft should be fairly ideal. You walk out onto the desert runway and cast a look at the sky. It is clear and there is no indication of wind. The temperature is rising, but it will not have any effect on you "upstairs." This is a day made to order for the big test.

The sleek research aircraft has been wheeled out and

spotted directly under the giant fuselage of the modified B-29. The mother ship has been jacked up in the air so the small plane can be wheeled in beneath it. During the dark hours before dawn the rocket craft has been fueled and polished and checked over for flaws of any type or size. Unless everything is in as perfect operating condition as man can make it, the flight will be canceled.

Even as you watch, the winches inside the spacious bomb bay of the B-29 start to whine. The small research craft is pulled up gently to snuggle against the underside of the big plane's fuselage, partly in, partly out.

You let your gaze wander to one side of the field and take in the radar antennae which will track your flight. Nearby a large trailer van also bristles with various wires and antennae. Inside are highly complicated telemetering devices and men sitting at control panels covered with banks of strange meters and flashing lights which only they understand. By remote control they will fly along with you, knowing everything that is happening to you and the plane long after you are lost from sight and sound. Other engineers are busy getting their radios hooked up. They, too, will follow every step of your flight by radio. They will not talk to you unless some emergency unknown to you shows up on the telemetering panels. But they will listen and record every word that you find time to utter during the flight.

The sight of two F-86 Sabre jet chase planes parked nearby comforts you. Such chase planes accompany all

Long after the Skyrocket is lost from sight and sound, its every move
is accurately tracked by ground radar.

flights of research aircraft. They observe your flight and
are often able to see things happening to your plane of
which you are unaware. They are good insurance. Besides,
it is nice to have company up there, although the chase
planes will not be able to stick with you very long, once
you have dropped away from the B-29 and started your
climb.

"Feeling O.K.?"

You turn to see the project co-ordinator standing beside you. He is one of the fellows who can cancel a flight

without bothering to give any explanation. Even if he thinks you had one too many eggs for breakfast he can wash out the flight. The taking of chances is kept to an absolute minimum in dealing with a man's life and a million-dollar airplane.

"Feel great," you say, smiling to hide the butterfly flutters in your stomach.

"Everything's checked out," he assures you. "So you might as well climb into your monkey suit."

The monkey suit is the T-1. Two groundmen help lace you into the skintight anti-G suit. You are far from comfortable, but a little discomfort is far preferable to the prospect of boiling in your own juices if the pressurized cockpit should spring a leak at high altitude.

An hour later you hoist yourself into the B-29. You look down at the rocket plane nestled snugly into the bomb bay. Soon the B-29 is grinding skyward on four motors. For a while you have nothing to do but sit and wait. You check over the flight plan which is on a clipboard strapped to your thigh. The plan is the essence of simplicity, calling for you to do only two things: fly as fast as you can and as high as you can.

Finally the pilot handling the B-29 nods back at you. You glance at a nearby altimeter. It reads almost 15,000 feet altitude. Time to go on oxygen. A few minutes later the pilot nods again and holds up two fingers. Twenty thousand feet. He is reminding you that it is time to climb into your supersonic steed.

Bill Bridgeman, research pilot, demonstrates the close quarters in insulated and instrument-filled cockpit of the supersonic Skyrocket.

A couple of the B-29 crewmen jump to your aid. They adjust the Martian-like pressure helmet on your head. They check the T-1 suit and escort you aft.

Gently, in order not to jam or tear anything, they help stuff you through the open hatch which leads into the research craft's small cockpit. There is a moment's pause while you take a deep breath. Holding it, you uncouple your oxygen hose from the B-29's tanks and plug it into the smaller plane's supply. Then your helpers snap the canopy down over your head and fasten it. You lock it from inside. Your only two connections with the outside world now are your radio and the winch cables which still hold you tight against the B-29's belly. Soon there will be just the one contact—radio. But there will be lots of ears hanging on each word and plenty of eyes reading your flight in the pulsating lines and flashing lights of the telemetering and radar apparatuses.

You settle yourself into the small bucket seat of the cramped cockpit quarters. You already have plugged in to the oxygen supply. Now you quickly plug in the radio leads and various electrical circuits which automatically control your pressure suit in case of emergency. You feel strangely like just another of the many instruments located all around and behind you. As a matter of fact, you are probably willing to admit that you are exactly that—an instrument like the rest of the gyros, pressure gauges, and other devices. After all, your purpose, like theirs, is to aid in guiding the man-carrying rocket projectile. One noteworthy difference, however, is that this instrument which goes by your name is also designed to eat hamburgers, swim, and enjoy an occasional evening at the movies.

You signal to the crew in the B-29 that you are secured and ready to go. Over the radio the pilot of the big plane tells you that it will be another thirty minutes or so before he can coax the heavily loaded mother ship up to 35,000 feet, at which altitude he plans to cut you loose.

The period of waiting is used to good advantage. You spend a few minutes "shadowboxing" the controls. You have spent hours doing it on the ground. In fact, you have made so many dry runs that you know exactly what you will do in the event of any emergency. One false motion, one switch pulled when it should be pushed, one moment of indecision, might turn escape into tragic imprisonment. You give a furtive glance to the one lever you hope you will not have to touch. It is the one that will blow you out of the aircraft, catapulting you away in the jettisonable sealed cockpit.

The jettisonable cockpit is strictly the last resort. It is not even included in all research-type aircraft. Although it looks like a sure thing on the drawing boards and mock-up tests under simulated flight conditions, there is really no telling exactly how the whole gadget will act if you should have to use it high up in the stratosphere while doing a neat 1000 miles an hour or so.

No, you don't want anything to do with that lever if you can help it.

Now you start reading down the check list strapped to your leg, gauge by gauge, instrument by instrument. You set some of them to correct positions. You merely note the presence of others. Once in flight, you will not have to worry about most of them. They register their readings automatically, and a camera located behind your back rest makes a complete film record of your flight.

You are concerned with a few instruments, however. For instance, the machometer which compares your own speed with the speed of sound will help you determine when to pour the juice to the rocket motors or when to ease off. A cluster of blind-flying instruments will help you maintain level flight after the horizon has been lost from view. Without the artificial horizon instrument you might be flying on your back, side, or in between without even being aware of it.

Of course, the bank of gauges which keeps you informed as to the condition of the rocket motor is a critical necessity. The cockpit air conditioner and the dehydrator which prevents the cockpit portholes from fogging up are important items. A small hand-operated windshield wiper fitted onto your helmet might well become a lifesaver if vapor should start condensing on the glass and impairing your vision.

One by one you check off the items. Faces peer in at you from the B-29—anxious faces searching for the least uncertainty that might be revealed in your expression or actions. It is definitely not too late to cancel the flight. If anyone in that plane sees one single thing which is not exactly as it should be, the flight will be washed out. Too much life, labor, and money are at stake to take any extra chances.

Now it is less than fifteen minutes to drop time. A message from the radar boys down on the ground tells the B-29 pilot that he is about eight miles east of the field and quartering into the wind. The pilot eases the climbing turn so that he is pointed more directly into the wind. He figures that, once he has cut you loose, a steep arching climb followed by the level speed run should take you about seven miles beyond the airfield and to windward. This should put you within easy gliding distance of home after the rockets burn out.

The B-29 is having trouble gaining more altitude. Heavily loaded, she is at her ceiling.

"All right," the pilot says over the radio. "I'll make one full circle, come up into the wind, and cut you loose. Everything O.K.?"

"Everything's O.K.," you assure him.

"Fine. Then let's make it five minutes to drop."

You clean up the final few chores of preparation. You check the automatic cockpit pressurizer. You also pressure-feed the rocket motor so that it will be ready for instant ignition once you drop away from the protecting mother ship.

You hear the B-29 pilot's announcement, "Four minutes." Then, "Three minutes, pal." And then, "Two."

You flick switches, turn knobs, adjust gadgets. The air conditioner starts to operate. One switch starts the automatic cameras whirring behind the back rest. You can hear the forced sigh of the rocket propellant as it presses through the fuel lines. The airplane is coming to life.

You sit there for a tense moment. You are certain you have overlooked nothing. You are ready. You say a little prayer, half aloud.

The B-29 pilot's voice comes into the earphones again. "One minute to drop!"

Skyrocket snuggled into the bomb bay of mother ship just prior to drop time. White vapor is indication that rocket motor is being primed for instant action.

Now you prime the rocket engine. Word from the engineers inside the B-29 tells you that the white vapor is oozing out astern. You can't see it, but they can. The rocket motor has taken the priming. It is all set to go.

"Forty seconds!"

You glance quickly again at the flight plan. There can be no guesswork on this flight. This is no Sunday drive.

"Twenty seconds!"

You set the steering yoke and rudder pedals in neutral position.

"Ten seconds . . . five seconds . . ."

Just time for a couple of fleeting thoughts as you reach toward the switch that fires rocket barrel number 1. It's cold outside . . . 65 degrees below zero. There's not enough oxygen out there to keep a fly alive for a minute. This has got to be done without a hitch. If anything goes wrong—

"Four . . . three . . . two . . . one . . ."

This is it!

"Drop!"

II

SKYROCKETING INTO THE UNKNOWN

A FAINT click reaches your ears as the B-29's bomb shackles release their grip upon your airplane. There is a momentary sinking feeling in the pit of your stomach as you drop free. Bright daylight suddenly streams into the cockpit. Without power, the rocket plane plummets downward like a boulder. But you already have your hand on the rocket switch. From a corner of your eye you see one of the Sabre jet chase planes off the port wing tip and fifty yards away.

Quickly you flick the switch that fires the number 1 rocket barrel. With the rocket motor, your speed is dependent upon whether you want to use one, two, three, or all four rocket tubes. Each tube produces 1500 pounds of thrust. Once fired, each tube burns with full power, and full power only. Therefore, you have a choice of four forward speeds.

There is a faint click as the bomb shackles release their grip and the
Skyrocket drops away from the mother ship.

Immediately a voice from the Sabre jet comes into your
earphones. "Number one firing O.K." The chase plane
pilot can see the flame spurting from the tail of your craft.

Inside the plane, you feel the 1500 pounds of single-
barrel thrust push their giant hand of pressure against
your back. You flip switches number 2, 3, and 4 in rapid
succession. You barely hear the Sabre jet pilot saying, "All
four firing, pal." Within eight seconds after the drop your
winged mount is trailing a superheated torch twice its own
length. The throaty roar of 6000 thrust pounds of drive is
loud in your ears.

Already you have started easing back on the steering

yoke. You have slightly over 4 tons of rocket propellant aboard. But the voracious tubes of the rocket motor gobble up over a ton a minute. Every second has to count if you hope to hit a record-breaking altitude and still have enough fuel left to level off and make your speed run.

The B-29, the F-86 chase plane, the earth—everything is quickly left behind. Pointing up at nearly a 35-degree angle, you see only the blue sky, a dustless, cloudless, dark blue that few earth men have ever seen. The sun is a dazzling disk of white in a deep azure setting.

But there is no time to look around. You do, however, sneak a quick glance at the slightly curving horizon of the Pacific Ocean. Although it is some fifty miles away, the curving shore line seems almost beneath you.

The airplane suddenly starts to shudder under the buffeting of the shock waves building up on the wings. You are entering the transonic zone, approaching the sonic wall. Nothing much to worry about, though. Airplanes such as the one you are flying have been through this so-called sonic barrier many times. You hit the roughest going just as your machometer reading is 1.0—the speed of sound.

A little gentle juggling of the controls, and you are through it. The path ahead is glassy slick. Any shock waves that the plane's speed creates now will be left far behind and out of the way. You are still climbing, and gaining speed in doing it. The spinning needle of the altimeter cannot seem to keep up with the rapid rate of climb.

In less than a minute you are approaching a speed of 1000 miles per hour. And you still have not leveled off for your speed dash.

A strange, unearthly silence has crept into the cockpit. Yet there is the faint whirring of the automatic camera behind the seat, the *whee-eep, whee-eep* sound of the laboring hydraulic pump force-feeding fuel into the flaming rockets. You can hear these sounds because they are traveling right along with you in the same cube of pressurized cockpit air. But all noises originating outside of the plane, or created by it, have dropped far away to the rear.

Soon you are streaking past the 60,000-foot level. However, other men have reached much higher altitudes than that. Even way back in 1935, two Army captains, Albert W. Stevens and Orvil A. Anderson, went aloft in a sealed globe hanging beneath an enormous gas bag named the Explorer II. They ascended to a record altitude of 72,395 feet before the free-flying balloon returned to earth. That record held until 1951 when William Bridgeman, in the Douglas Skyrocket, reached a new height of 79,494 feet.

But you are not concerning yourself with breaking records. After all, record breaking is incidental to a research flier's real purpose. The real purpose is being recorded by the electric cameras and by the hundreds of stress-and-strain gauges scattered throughout the airplane. It is being recorded by clusters of other electronic instruments which crowd the airplane from pointed nose to

Skyrocketing into the unknown.

flaming stern. This is the type of data which aircraft builders and pilots of the future must know.

On the subject of space, you realize that you have already climbed beyond the protection of the troposphere. If anything goes wrong now that will expose you to the frigid outside temperature or to the thin atmosphere, you can last a very few seconds.

The research plane is spearing majestically into space . . . even gaining more speed as she climbs into the more rarefied atmosphere. But you left the B-29 mother ship over two minutes ago. Your fuel is over half gone. About time to start bending over for your straight speed run.

You ease the yoke forward, nosing over gently toward

217

level flight. You watch the accelerometer dial closely. You must not bend over too fast. You can't take much of the negative-G without redding out. The safety harness tugs at you, keeping your head from going out through the canopy as the plane pushes over. The blood surging upward into your head leaves a tingling sensation in your blood-starved legs and body. Easy now! Not too much!

As soon as you reach level flight, you quit thinking about the instruments. There are other things demanding your attention. The instruments can take care of themselves.

The rockets are roaring at full power, although you are aware only of the thrust, not the sound. Your guess is that you are whizzing along in the neighborhood of 1200 miles per hour. Yet, without anything outside on which to focus your eyes, you have the feeling of almost standing still . . . suspended in limitless space. Ever since passing the sound barrier you have been sailing smoothly, in the absence of turbulence-creating shock waves.

Then, just as you are about to sit back and enjoy the ultrasonic speed dash, something happens. The airplane suddenly dips its left wing sharply. Then it rocks back in the other direction—back and forth, back and forth. This rocking motion, called lateral oscillation, becomes more severe as each wing dips deeper and deeper and the plane approaches a vertical position, threatening to roll completely over. It pitches and bucks. The controls seem useless.

Danger crowds the cockpit. Perhaps there is not enough body to the air outside for the controls to operate. Perhaps, too, there is a second barrier, worse than the initial sound barrier. Perhaps that second barrier appears as you approach or exceed Mach 2.0, twice the speed of sound.

Certainly the skies have not yet revealed more than a small part of their mysteries . . . or dangers.

"Easy," you tell yourself. "This is no place to lose your head."

You don't dare throttle back suddenly. Such a maneuver might throw the airplane into a dangerous side-slipping, snakelike yaw. Or it might cause it to tuck under in an outside loop, out of control. Either maneuver might quickly prove disastrous.

It is difficult to know what to do. Fairly similar conditions have been encountered by test fliers before you. But each flight unfolds new complications. There are no cut-and-dried notes or instructions to go by.

Your only course is to try riding it out. You move the controls delicately, like a concert violinist coaxing a melody from a Stradivarius. For a few uncertain moments, the airplane threatens to have its own uncontrolled way. Then slowly, as an even higher speed is reached, the rocket craft responds to your bidding and levels its wings.

There is still another immediate threat. Although the outside temperature is around 65 degrees below zero, the friction of the thin air brushing against the outside skin of the airplane at over 1200 miles an hour is creating a blistering heat on the outer surfaces. Already, despite the laboring efforts of the refrigeration unit, you can feel the heat start to seep into the cockpit. If it continued for any length of time, it might roast you alive.

But not this time. You are not carrying enough fuel for sustained ultrasonic flight. You have barely become concerned with the heat when the rocket motor suddenly arrives at burnout. It coughs unevenly as the final quarts of the liquid oxygen and alcohol-water mixture squirt through the fuel lines. You immediately cut the switches, to prevent the gasping rocket motor from sending the plane bucking through the sky.

A slight shudder goes through the airplane. It warns that you are slowing down, backing out of the supersonic and into the subsonic zone of speed.

But there is still a job ahead. The field must be many miles away and perhaps fifteen miles or more below. Fuel is gone; power is gone. Patches of clouds you had not seen before now hide much of the earth from view. Your job is to find the airfield, manage to reach it without benefit of any power, and make a safe landing on a dead stick.

With lots of weight, no power, and hardly any wing to hold you aloft, the airplane plummets earthward at an alarming rate.

During several lonesome miles on the way down from an area in the stratosphere where man has seldom been, you have a little time to think. Although you do not know the exact official figures, you feel confident that you have just completed one of man's farthest journeys into the lower fringes of space. Perhaps, too, you have reached a speed in doing it that is a new first in the rapidly expanding field of supersonics. You feel more than a little humble and reverent. Despite what you may have achieved, you have made no more than the tiniest of scratches on the surface of the limitless space of our universe. Had your flight been a thousand miles higher—or a hundred thousand—it would still have been only a step toward the journey into the great void of nothingness. There is reason to feel humble and reverent.

Suddenly a friendly and welcome voice comes into your earphones. "Where've you been, boy?" it asks cheerily. "Don't you know lunch is gettin' cold?"

You grin to yourself and glance out of one of the cockpit portholes. The Sabre jet chase plane is just off to your right, flying wing to wing. "Relax, pal," the pilot calls again. "I'll lead you home."

That is exactly what happens. The Sabre leads you through the cloud bank. As you break through the final low banners of white, the desert spreads out below in a sage-and-cactus-covered carpet of grayish tan. In the distance, but not too far, a cluster of miniature buildings and a long worn strip across the smooth dry lake mark the location of Edwards Air Force Base.

But the job is not finished yet. Just gliding without power, the heavy research plane is doing a neat 270 miles per hour. You must judge the field exactly right. Together,

Coasting home after fuel is exhausted, the Skyrocket is picked up by an F-86 Sabre jet chase plane, which leads the way back to the field.

Approaching the field, the Skyrocket lowers landing wheels preparatory to a hot 180-mile-per-hour dead-stick landing.

rocket plane and Sabre jet start into the downwind leg at the amazingly high altitude of 15,000 feet—higher than many small planes can fly, let alone start their landing approach. You lower the wheels and make a ninety-degree turn into your base leg. You hold on course for a few fast

223

miles. Then you make another ninety-degree turn and come up into the wind on the final approach. Cactus and sagebrush scoot past beneath you in a blur. This soon gives way to the smooth, spotless sand of the dry lake.

The pilot of the chase plane keeps talking you down, telling you things that your limited visibility hides from view. The all-important item of the dead-stick approach is to avoid falling into a stall. To prevent this, you fairly dive for the field. Then, when the ground seems close enough to reach out and touch, you bring the plane's nose up.

"You got her, pal," the chase plane pilot informs you jubilantly. "Keep your nose right where she is. You're ten feet from terra firma." With these final words, the Sabre peels off into the sky, leaving the whole desert floor to you.

Clocking a hot 180 miles an hour, you set the tricycle landing gear down as softly as a feather dropping on a Persian rug. You keep playing the controls. Now you are a race driver trying to keep your speeding aircraft from skidding sideways or turning over. Slowly you bring her to a stop. You unplug yourself from the various circuits, unfasten your safety straps, climb out, and wait for the convoy of trucks and jeeps that are racing across the dry lake toward you. It's all over now but the shouting.

Later, after the engineers and scientists have read, deciphered, interpreted, checked, and confirmed the enormous stock of data which has been automatically telemetered and collected during your flight, you will know just where you stand among your high-and-fast-flying brethren of the sky.

It was under the same general conditions as those of your flight that Major Charles (Chuck) Yeager, on August 14, 1947, became the first man in the history of the world to fly faster than the speed of sound. His record speed of 967 miles per hour was accomplished in the Bell X-1 under the same conditions—launched in mid-air from the bomb bay of a mother ship.

Major Yeager's record flight fostered a friendly competition among other airmen who were interested in supersonic flying, and that brought about amazing achievements and invaluable aviation knowledge in the years that followed.

On August 15, 1951, after several high-altitude supersonic jaunts in the Douglas D-558-2, Test Pilot William (Bill) Bridgeman speared the sleek white Skyrocket through the thin upper atmosphere at an unprecedented speed of 1238 miles per hour. Adding more laurels to man's achievements in the air, Bridgeman took the same airplane up to the equally unheard-of altitude of 79,494 feet into the stratosphere.

For a while these two records appeared to be the ultimate in what modern aviation research and aircraft construction could accomplish. For two years all attempts to surpass the two marks failed. Then in the latter part of 1953, the year that marked the 50th anniversary of flight as dated from the Wright brothers' first 120-foot jaunt off the sand dune near Kitty Hawk, the lid fairly blew off of what had seemed man's limitations in the air.

It was just over two years since Bill Bridgeman had gained title to both the speed and altitude records when Lieutenant Colonel Marion E. Carl of the United States Marine Corps came back into the record-breaking picture. It will be recalled that Carl, when a major back in 1947, had established an official low-altitude world's speed record of 650.7 miles per hour in the Douglas Skystreak, a forerunner of the rocket-powered Skyrocket.

On August 31, 1953, Lieutenant Colonel Carl climbed into the same Skyrocket in which Bridgeman had set his two marks. Employing the almost standard procedure of being carried aloft by a mother ship, the Marine flier cut loose at an altitude of 34,000 feet. Blasting away with all four rocket tubes, he aimed skyward. As he reached a height of 75,000 feet, the final pints of fuel coughed through the rocket motor. Yet the Skyrocket's upward momentum was so great that even with a dead motor it coasted on up to a new altitude mark of 83,235 feet— nearly 16 miles—before gravity tipped the nose down and Lieutenant Colonel Carl headed back to the field on a dead stick.

Nor was Bill Bridgeman's speed record destined to hold up any longer. During the two years since he had established his mark, the Skyrocket had undergone certain modifications and improvements in the NACA hangars. Their exact nature was a secret, as are most phases of research aviation until the sharing of knowledge is deemed worthwhile and safe.

The refinements in the Skyrocket, plus the skill and daring of NACA's pilot, Scott Crossfield, were sufficient to establish a new claim to the high-altitude speed title. On October 14, 1953 (the sixth anniversary of Major Chuck Yeager's history-making first flight through sound), Crossfield slanted the Skyrocket upward at about a. 40-degree angle after leaving the B-29. Reaching an altitude of 62,000 feet, he leveled off and started his all-out speed dash.

By the time he had glided back to Edwards Air Force Base, Crossfield was holder of a new all-time air-speed record of 1272 miles per hour, 32 miles an hour faster than Bridgeman's long-standing mark.

Since he had made over 50 flights in the Skyrocket, Crossfield felt that the airplane still had not given everything it had. A month later he had another try at wringing out the last ounce of speed. After leaving the B-29, he lifted the Skyrocket to 60,000 feet, leveled off and "let her go." In the quiet world of supersonic speed, the Skyrocket lanced through the stratosphere. Crossfield glanced at his machometer. He was amazed to note that it indicated better than Mach 2, twice the speed of sound. Yet he was experiencing sensations no different than if he were flying at around 850 miles per hour in that smooth area beyond the turbulence of the sound barrier.

He held his Mach 2 speed for nearly ten seconds before

the burnout. Again he took the fast coasting route home, to learn happily that he had broken his own month-old speed mark by establishing a new one of 1320 miles per hour.

Even while the Skyrocket and the men who flew her seemed to be making a clean sweep in the fields of high-altitude and high-speed flight, another research airplane was trundled out onto the concrete apron in front of the Air Force hangar at the desert test base. Large figures near its pointed nose designated it as the Bell X-1A. It appeared to be very similar to the X-1, the first supersonic plane. However, on closer inspection differences showed up. The X-1A is nearly five feet longer than its predecessor. This increases the tank space for additional rocket fuel. The X-1A is also equipped with an improved turbine pump to force-feed the rocket propellant into the hungry motor, resulting in higher efficiency and more power. No doubt there are other innovations not yet revealed to the public.

It was only wise and fitting that Major Charles (Chuck) Yeager be allowed to see what the X-1A could do. After all, he had been the first man to fly faster than sound, had done it many times in the years following that memorable day, and knew more about piloting the Bell-built products than any other man.

On December 12, 1953, Major Yeager dropped away from the bomb bay of the mother ship at the usual altitude of 30,000 feet. He cut in three of the four rocket barrels and headed up in a climbing arc. At 45,000 feet he switched on the fourth rocket tube. Widening the arc, he climbed in a gently curving trajectory. At an altitude of 70,000 feet he reached the point where his flight arc leveled off and started downward. In the instant during level flight, and just before the rocket motor reached burn out, the X-1A hit its maximum speed.

Then a terrifying thing happened. At approximately Mach 2.5, two and a half times the speed of sound, the X-1A suddenly went completely out of control and even as Major Yeager was feeling great concern over the unusual experience of actually seeing the shock waves forming off his wings, the X-1A began plummeting downward through the stratosphere in wild uncontrolled gyrations. It rolled, pitched, and yawed sideways as the research pilot tried every trick in the book and some not in it in an attempt to bring the airplane back to some semblance of obedience.

It was not until he had fallen nearly ten horrible, nerve-shattering miles that he was able to bring the X-1A under control again and continue his fast-speed glide back to the safety of the airfield.

Major Yeager's flight was significant in two respects: one a welcome result, the other a factor which is creating considerable concern and uneasiness among both the builders and the fliers of high ultrasonic research aircraft.

The welcome news was the fact that at his point of maximum speed Major Yeager had again pushed back the stubbornly resisting frontier of ultrasonic speed. He had reached a speed of 1650 miles per hour, 330 miles an hour faster than Scott Crossfield's three-week-old record mark.

But several big questions arose as a result of Major Yeager's having lost control of the X-1A at its amazing speed of two and a half times that of sound. Had Major Yeager opened up a new hazard? Is there a limit along the speed spectrum beyond which conventional airplane controls completely lose their effect? Had the research craft, in pushing back the speed frontier to 1650 miles per hour, taken too big a stride forward before every step leading up to it had become thoroughly known? What might happen at Mach 3? Had the shock waves Major Yeager saw forming off the wings at Mach 2.5 indicated another barrier, "multisonic" or otherwise? Perhaps a more solid barrier, and one that is even more treacherous than the heat barrier, lies somewhere beyond. Perhaps Major Yeager had nudged it.

With slow deliberation aeronautical scientists, engineers, and research pilots are presently searching for the answers to these questions. They are searching in the D-558-2, the X-1A, X-1B, and the newer swept-wing speedster, the X-2.

They have no fear of the new hazards that seem to lie ahead, but they do have great respect for them. They have found the answers to many of the old problems. They are confident that, little by little, they will find the answers to the new ones. After all, that is the purpose of research

Major Charles E. Yeager alights from one of his many test flights in the Bell X-1A to be congratulated by the builder, Lawrence D. Bell.

flying. Such subjects as a speed of 1650-miles-per-hour flights or sky-piercing jaunts to altitudes of 83,235 feet make handy topics of conversation. To the man on the street that is about all they are. To the airman their significance is different.

Tomorrow the figures may be as obsolete as the dodo bird, yet their real purpose of adding to the ever-increasing progress in the air will remain firm and worthwhile.

12

WHERE TO NEXT?

IT is generally assumed by today's cosmic-minded public that the next step in aviation will be the conquest of outer space. "Why not?" they ask. After all, only a few short years ago men believed that any aircraft would shatter itself against the so-called sonic barrier and that no frail man-carrying object could pierce it. Yet already a man has flown at two-and-a-half times the speed of sound. Airplanes now on planning boards and even in the testing stages are perhaps destined to shatter all existing records. This may become increasingly difficult, for apparently there is no limit to the number and seriousness of obstacles in the sky. But progress thrives on a full share of hazards and men readily accept the challenge.

Helpful to man's knowledge are the ingenious experiments and mechanical contrivances that have subjected him to tests enormously more severe than surviving

High-speed jet transports similar to those illustrated here are already taking to the skies.

Mach 2.5. These tests have proved that the human body can withstand pressures and strains far greater than science had dared dream of five years ago. If the get-away speed, or initial velocity, of a vehicle is gradual enough not to break his bones or compress him into a pancake, it seems that there is no limit to the speed which the human body can endure. Of course, since he will travel inside of the sealed capsule of a space ship, the capsule, not the man, will be subject to most of the strain.

Northrop Aircraft Company's YB-49 Flying Wing is an eight-jet research craft used in testing one possible design of the future airplane.

One pilot tells about the ordinary housefly that rode with him on one of his high-altitude supersonic test flights. The pilot did not even notice the hitchhiking fly until they were up around 60,000 feet and doing about 1000 miles an hour. The fly rode it out perched calmly on the inside of the windshield. Within the protection of the pressurized cockpit the fly seemed as much at home as though he were on a back-porch screen.

After the landing had been made, the housefly buzzed away happily, no doubt to boast to his winged friends of being the only high-altitude supersonic fly in the world.

If the human body is furnished with an artificial atmosphere similar to that near the earth, there seems to be no limit to the distance in space where it can survive. Pressurized cockpits and artificial breathing facilities fill its needs at present. Although today's methods may be laughed at as primitive by future space men, the necessity for atmospheric pressure and oxygen will always remain. Despite all mechanical progress the needs of the human body remain constant.

There are few denials among men of science that space travel—even interplanetary travel—is certain to become a future reality. Famous astronomers declare that the person destined to make the first trip to some celestial body, probably the moon, is right now playing around the back yard in rompers. It is a fairly common belief that man will make his first space voyage around 1990. By that time most of the problems of space travel and human survival will have been ironed out. These men of vision urge educational groups to start immediately preparing young people for an age of interplanetary travel. Only through long preparation and study can most problems be solved.

Seeming to share this belief, several colleges have added undergraduate courses devoted to studying the problems of space travel. Dealing with rocketry, space-ship design, and the numerous human elements connected with space travel, such courses will no doubt find their way into the curricula of an ever increasing number of schools.

Imaginary air terminal of the future, with runways 20,000 feet long, helicopter facilities, underground parking and freight handling.

Other rocket and space-travel scientists support varying theories on the whens and hows of space travel. Some science writers and space authorities believe that planting a space station a thousand miles out from earth is a present-day possibility. However, the enormous task of construction and the fabulous expense involved may delay the project for a considerable time. Much of the necessary knowledge is now at hand; much must still be learned.

Physiologists, men interested in the human factors involved in space travel, say that any youth in good health can become suitable space-crew material. He or she must, however, undergo years of highly specialized training and education toward a career in astronautics. Advanced mathematics, physics, and astronomy will be three highly important courses for the ambitious space voyager. In addition, a thorough knowledge of biology and space medicine will be necessary. After all, human beings will be a part of any real space travel. It is only good common sense that their physical welfare should receive full attention.

The same people who predict the approaching age of space travel are the first ones to add a cautious, "Slow down, Buck Rogers. We're not there yet."

As a matter of fact, we are quite a distance away. In theory, no. In theory we have already built artificial satellites a thousand miles out in space. In theory we have practically transplanted a colony of celestial pioneers on the moon. In theory, that is.

But there is quite a gap between theory and fact, especially when dealing with such a fantastic field as space travel. The paths leading to the stars are cluttered with obstacles. High-altitude and supersonic flights of modern aircraft such as the Skyrocket, the X-1A, and the X-2 and of exploratory missiles such as the V-2, the Martin Viking, the Aerobee, and others have furnished much valuable data concerning the enormity of several obstacles.

The temperature created by solar radiation—4000 degrees at an altitude of 400 miles—can perhaps be controlled to some extent by using non-heat-absorbing paints or materials on the sunward side of space ships. New insulations may also repel the torrid rays. How well this heat can be controlled remains a challenge to present-day and future scientists. They also have a king-sized job in furnishing protection to both man and machine from the billions of unfiltered cosmic rays which constantly bombard outer space. It is believed that the belt of dangerous radiation is a thin one, however, and that once through it man will find himself in a temperatureless void of nothingness. There are many conflicting beliefs regarding this theory. More definite answers must be acquired before man will be sent aloft.

Not so uncertain a hazard, however, is friction heat, or the thermal barrier. Any high-speed vehicle, even today's supersonic airplane, encounters this obstacle. If such craft as the Skyrocket or X-1A carried sufficient fuel to sustain flight for any length of time, the friction heat probably would melt both plane and pilot. In space travel the hazard of the thermal barrier would be magnified many times.

It has been established that in order to escape the pull of earth's gravity a rocket would have to generate a getaway speed, or escape velocity, of some 26,000 miles per hour, approximately 7 miles per second. It would have to build up this fantastic speed in a matter of seconds after leaving the launching ramp. Once this speed is reached, no further power is needed to aid the vehicle in escaping the earth's gravity. It will coast from there on.

With unlimited fuel capacity, a rocket ship could leave

the earth at a much slower speed, building up its momentum gradually. Nevertheless, its speed would have to reach thousands of miles per hour.

The air brushing against a present-day airplane traveling at 1000 miles an hour builds up a sizzling 200 degrees of friction heat on the plane's outer surface. Multiply that several times—up to 26 times—and the friction heat is sufficient to make a cinder out of the best-laid plans—or planes. In fact, 26,000 miles an hour is a rate of travel faster than that of many meteors, and the blazing streaks in the night skies testify to the fate of a meteor when it reaches even the thinnest outer boundary of the stratosphere.

Of course, when the moon ship reaches the perfect vacuum of outer space, where there is no air to brush against it, there will be no friction heat. Getting out there with enough velocity to keep going and not turn into a spark while doing it is a real problem.

The speed of a rocket depends pretty much upon its jet velocity. As mentioned earlier, the jet velocity is the speed with which the hot gases leave the jet nozzle. It is limited by the ability of fuels to generate super-hot gases. Only one fuel mixture which is not excessively expensive has been capable of building up a jet velocity of over 8000 miles per hour. This is a mixture of hydrogen and fluorine. It burns so hot in producing this velocity, however, that practically every known metal or ceramic melts or disintegrates under its blaze.

To produce a fuel three times as powerful and to fur-

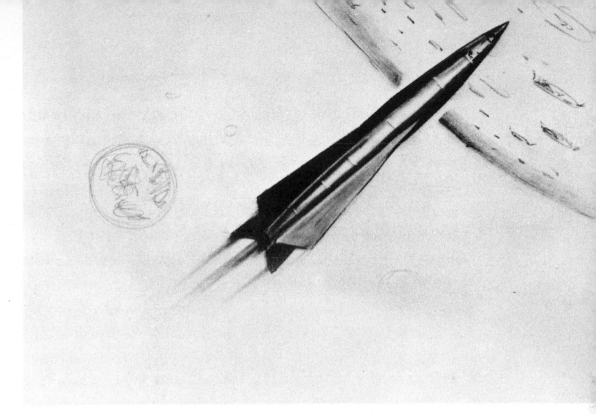

Space ships are not probable during the next quarter century. Rockets to the moon, with no passengers, will perhaps be the first step in space travel.

There is little likelihood of the existence of flying saucers unless the circle replaces the delta as a wing form.

nish rocket tubes which would stand up under its blazing fury are all but beyond the dreams of present-day scientists. Of course, a rocket can build up speed equivalent to nearly twice the jet velocity of the fuel if it can carry enough fuel to continue a prolonged speed-increasing thrust as the rocket's weight decreases. But rockets are fantastically thirsty. It is estimated that, even using the best fuels now known to man, it would take more than 400 pounds of fuel to propel a single pound of rocket, instruments, or human weight beyond the pull of the earth's gravity.

Since it would be impossible to make a container that would weigh less than a pound and yet be able to carry 400 pounds of fuel, the entire plan seems to fall apart before it gets well started.

Some authorities figure that atomic power will be the eventual answer to the fuel problem. Yet an atomic pile, plus heavy armor to protect space ship and occupants from deadly radiation, would weigh a great deal—possibly enough to defeat its own purpose.

Multiple-step rockets may be another answer. Each fuel-carrying section would drop away as its cargo was exhausted. By the time the final crew-carrying section took over, it would be far enough out in space and have sufficient momentum to make it possible for it to continue the journey to the moon.

The multiple-step rocket might also solve the friction-heat problem. By building up its speed more gradually—

Powered by a double-turbine turboprop engine, the Lockheed XFV-1
is capable of taking off vertically, leveling off for high-speed flight,
hovering, and making a pinpoint landing by backing straight down.
Twin propellers spin in opposite directions.

the speed of each successive stage added to that of the previous one—the enormous escape velocity would be unnecessary.

But how is man going to live and how is he going to get back home after he has arrived at the soundless, alternately scorching and freezing wastes of the moon or some other planet also almost totally lacking in atmosphere? The rocket would have to be capable of making a round trip.

Even if such a rocket could be built, the cost in millions of dollars staggers the imagination. Although space travel to other planets will no doubt come to pass, it is going to take time and immeasurable study, skill, and financing.

There is, however, a more immediate and practical application of space travel. Travel through space can be accomplished without having to worry about escaping the pull of gravity. After all, what we know as space—a resistless vacuum of nothingness—begins at an altitude of about 120 miles. This is not far at all, since we have become accustomed to talking about millions of miles or even casually mentioning a light year now and then in our everyday conversations on space flight.

So why not build aircraft that can make use of this vacuum without aspiring to reach Venus or the moon? Since you are not attempting to escape gravity, none of those amazing speeds which might turn you into a cinder are necessary. Your stratosphere liner could be quite similar to the standard design of modern high-speed airplanes.

The XFV-1 being lifted into take-off position by a special ground handling cart.

Rocket transport may cross oceans in one to two hours and reach altitudes of several hundred miles. Will require great improvement in fuels and solution of the problems of aerodynamic heating when re-entering the earth's atmosphere.

The plane would fly in a long arching trajectory. Perhaps its wings would fold back or retract most of the way during the highest and fastest part of its journey. It would climb into space, probably using jet power until the atmosphere became too thin to support combustion. Then it would switch to rockets. Once in space, it would level off, boost its speed to a couple of thousand miles an hour, and keep on rocket power until time to shut off the motors and make the long slanting high-speed glide to the distant port. The jets would take over again for the final approach

The delta jet transport, with a cruising altitude of 40,000 to 60,000 feet, is a good possibility for supersonic travel, but will require great development of engines, both atomic and jet.

and landing. In this manner a trip from Los Angeles to New York might take less than two hours. Breakfast in Dallas, Texas, and lunch in Paris, France, would be the order of the day.

This is the sort of thing toward which air-minded men are striving at present. Higher altitudes and faster speeds have their practical uses right here on our own planet, Earth. For remember, man has always been a restless creature. Now he has found that he can get from one place to another in less time by going higher, where there is little or no air to slow him down.

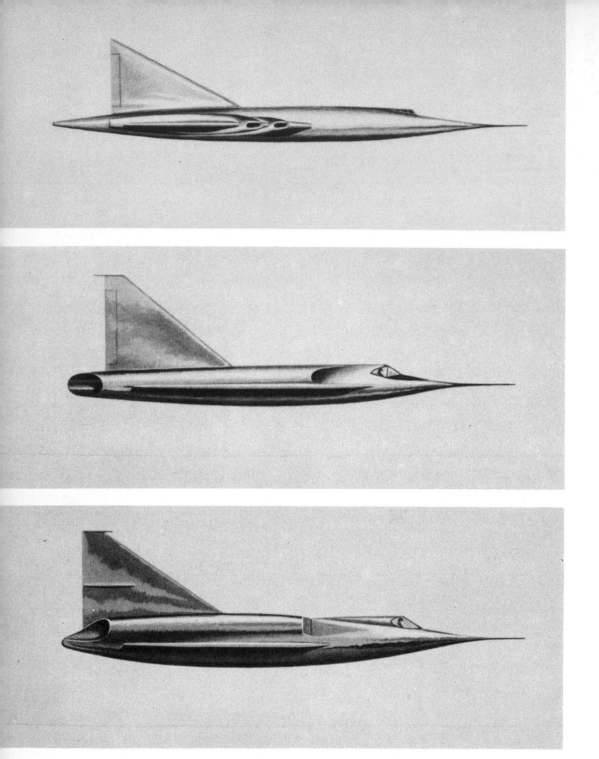

Three profiles of proposed jet airplanes of the coming years.

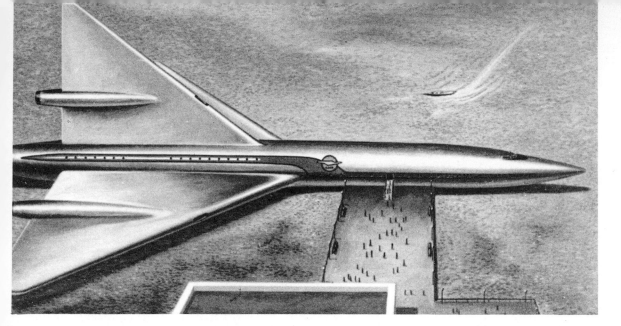

The stratosphere transport of the future may be suprisingly similar to the modern delta-wing type aircraft.

Consequently you can be sure he will keep striving to go higher and faster. For many years he probably will be concentrating on overcoming the various obstacles created by the gravity and atmosphere of his own planet. But some day in the future man will plunge forth into outer space.

Each progressive step in modern aviation, although having its practical present-day usages, tends more and more toward ultrasonic speeds and increasingly high altitudes. Strangely, or perhaps not so strangely, these are the very two items which are of utmost importance to space travel.

It will be a long, rough road. Airplanes such as the ones viewed in action in this book have gone the first few miles along this road leading into space. The men of vision who build them and the men of action and courage who fly them are finding valuable indications of what lies ahead.

But the journey has just begun. It will take many a

249

good rocket ship, many a good man and woman to plan, build, and fly them. This creates no big worry. Wherever there have been goals worth achieving, there have always been men and women striving to gain them. There is no reason to believe it will be any different in the future.

One thing is certain. In this day and age, there are few—very few—people who will say the sky's the limit . . . and mean it.

For the future lies beyond.

INDEX

251

INDEX